Sounds of Our HERITAGE

from the Great Lakes

BILL MARTIN, JR.
General Editor

BERNARD J. WEISS
Senior Author, Holt Basic Reading

Holt, Rinehart and Winston, Publishers
New York • Toronto • London • Sydney

Acknowledgments

The authors and Holt, Rinehart and Winston, Publishers, thank the following publishers, authors, agents, and parties whose help and permission to reprint materials have made this book possible. If any errors in acknowledgments have occurred, the errors were inadvertent and will be corrected in subsequent editions as they are realized.

Atheneum Publishers for *Chants and Images from Indians and Eskimos of North America* edited by James Houston (A Margaret K. McElderry Book). Copyright © 1972 by James Houston. Used by permission.

Doubleday & Company, Inc. for excerpt adapted from *Copper-Toed Boots* by Marguerite de Angeli. Copyright © 1932 by Marguerite de Angeli. Used by permission.

Follett Publishing Company, a division of Follett Corporation, for adaptation of "Where Are the Cowboys, George" from *Tales of the Elders* by Carol Ann Bales. Copyright © 1977 by Carol Ann Bales. For excerpted adaptation of "Jane Addams and Hull House" from *Jane Addams* by Elizabeth C. Mooney. Copyright © 1968 by Elizabeth Mooney. Used by permission.

Harper & Row, Publishers for excerpted adaptation of "The Widow Oakley's Daughter, Annie" from *The Ohio Story* by Frank Siedel. Copyright © 1950 by The World Publishing Company. For excerpted selection "Dance at Grandpa's" from *Little House in the Big Woods* by Laura Ingalls Wilder. Text copyright 1932 by Laura Ingalls Wilder, renewed © 1959 by Roger L. McBride. Used by permission.

Holt, Rinehart and Winston, Publishers for excerpted adaptation of "The Ice Man and the Messenger of Springtime" from *Tepee Tales of the American Indian* by Dee Brown. Copyright © 1979 by Dee Brown. Used by permission.

Houghton Mifflin Company for adapted excerpted selection "Johnny Appleseed" from *Yankee Doodle's Cousins* by Anne Malcolmson. Copyright 1941 by Anne Burnett Malcolmson. Renewed © 1969 by Anne Malcolmson von Storch. Used by permission.

Harvey C. Jacobs for adapted excerpted selection "Bringing in the Sheaves" from *We Came Rejoicing* by Harvey C. Jacobs. Copyright © 1967 by Harvey C. Jacobs. Used by permission.

Lenniger Literary Agency, Inc., 250 West 57th Street, New York, N.Y. 10107, author's agents, for "Why the Woodpecker Has a Red Head" from *Let the Moon Go By* by Emma Gelders Sterne. Copyright © 1955 by Emma Gelders Sterne. Used by permission.

Little, Brown and Company for "Hide-and-Seek Chants and 3 Riddles" by Duncan Emrich from *Folklore on the American Land* by Duncan Emrich. Copyright © 1972 by Duncan Emrich. Used by permission.

The Macmillan Company for adapted excerpted selection "The Willow Basket" from *Magical Melons* by Carol Ryrie Brink. Copyright 1939, 1944 by Macmillan Publishing Co., renewed © 1967, 1968, 1972 by Carol Ryrie Brink. For excerpted adapted selection "Prunestones and Coffee Grounds" (Paul Bunyan Invents the Shift System) from *The Legends of Paul Bunyan* by Roberta Strauss Feuerlicht. Copyright © 1966 by The Macmillan Company. Used by permission.

The Ohio Historical Society, Inc. for adapted excerpted selection "Pone, Cake, Dodger, and Mush" from *Echoes*, Vol. 5, No. 10, October 1966. Also "Some Pioneer Customs" from *Prevailing Manners and Customs of the Frontiers* by Irene Hardy, from *Ohio History*, Vol. 86 Winter, 1977, No. 1. Used by permission.

G. P. Putnam's Sons for excerpted adaptation from *Chicago Burns* by Sonia Fox. Copyright © 1971 by Sonia Fox. Used by permission.

Charles Scribner's Sons for adapted excerpted selection "Abe Lincoln, Growing Up" from *Abraham Lincoln, an Initial Biography* by Genevieve Foster. Copyright 1950 by Genevieve Foster. Used by permission.

The Viking-Penguin Press for adapted excerpted selection "Mike Fink, the River Roarer" from *American Tall Tales* by Adrien Stoutenberg. Copyright © 1966 by Adrien Stoutenberg. Used by permission.

Any material on evolution presented in this book is presented as theory rather than fact.

Photo Credits

COVER: (right) "The Pioneers" by William Ranney, Courtesy, Knoedler & Co., Inc. & the Joselson Collection; (top left) Shostal Associates; (bottom left) Alvis Upitis/The Image Bank.

UNIT 1:   pp.8–9 State Historical Society of Wisconsin; p.24 NCR Corporation; p.28 (top) The Massillon Museum, Ohio, (middle) Abby Aldrich Rockefeller Folk Art Center, (bottom) State Historical Society of Wisconsin; p.29 (top) International Harvester Company, (middle) Greenfield Village, Henry Ford Museum, (bottom) State Historical Society of Wisconsin; p.30 (top) H. W. Pierce/Library of Congress, (middle left) Deere and Company, (middle right) Michigan Travel Commission; p.31 (top) State Historical Society of Wisconsin, (middle) Edger William and Berneice Chrysler Garbisch Collection, National Gallery of Art, (bottom) Roscoe Village/Ohio Office of Travel and Tourism.

UNIT 2: pp.50–51 Minnesota Historical Society; p.59 The Bettmann Archive; p.62 (top) John Wells/University of Chicago, (middle) Michigan Travel Bureau, (bottom) Focus on Sports; p.63 (top) Field Museum of Natural History, (middle) National Park Service, (bottom) Michigan Travel Commission; p.64 (top) John G. Shedd Aquarium, (middle left) Halstead/Stewart, City of Detroit Office of Public Information, (middle right) Ohio Office of Travel and Tourism, (bottom) Indianapolis Motor Speedway; p.65 (top) Wisconsin Natural Resources Department, (bottom) The Ohio Historical Society, Inc.

UNIT 3: pp.76–77 H. D. Ellis/Mackinac Bridge Authority; p.93 University of Illinois Library at Chicago Circle; p.94 The Bettmann Archive; p.95 Deere and Company; p.96 (top) Appel Color Photography, (middle) Webb Photos, (bottom) Shostal Associates; p.97 (top left) Cleveland-Cliffs Iron Company, (top right) Appel Color Photography, (bottom) Michigan Travel Commission; p.98 (top) Frank Cezus/Black Star, (middle) Mackinaw Island Park Commission, (bottom) Illinois Department of Conservation; p.99 (top) Cleveland-Cliffs Iron Company, (bottom left) American Dairy Association of Wisconsin, (bottom right) Michigan Department of Natural Resources; p.105 State Historical Society of Wisconsin; p.108 Library of Congress.

UNIT 4: pp.116–117 State Historical Society of Wisconsin; p.121 Buffalo Bill Memorial Museum; p.128 (top left) the Metropolitan Museum of Art, (top right) Library of Congress, (bottom) Library of Congress; p.129 (top left to right) Library of Congress, Library of Congress, Hudson Historical Bureau, Library of Congress. (bottom left to

TABLE OF
CONTENTS

5

A Canal Dance

One night in Cleveland we had a dance,
On the weight-lock platform we did prance,
It was ice cream, cake, O what a time;
In a little while the sun did shine.

Ha, ha, ha, ha, O what fun!
We had that night, yes, every one,
The mules would winnow, kick and prance.
They tried so hard to join our dance.

Well, I'm up in years, yet young, young, young,
But a better life could never come;
Let others do as they choose, dear pal,
But I will stay on the old canal!

Anonymous

arrowroots
(ar' ō rüts')
plants that grow
in the shape of
the head of an
arrow

Why the Woodpecker Has a Red Head

Collected by Emma Gelders Sterne

The tribe of the Algonquians was scattered
over the land around the Great Lakes. They lived
in houses made of poles covered with cedar bark.
Some of the houses were large enough for three
families.

The Algonquians had plenty of food. They had
corn from their planting and bittersweet bark for
soup. They had arrowroots and waterlily buds to
eat. They also hunted in the forest for meat, and
caught fish in the lakes.

The Algonquians had a special friend. Many of
their stories were about him. His name is
Manabozho. Some of the stories tell about the
tricks he played on the Indians. He was known
by other names, too. Two of them are Nanabush
and Winabijou. The stories about him have been
handed down from generation to generation.

The Algonquians gathered on the long
platforms in their houses to hear the history of

this giant character. Someone would say, "When I was a boy, this is what the old men told me that their fathers told them when they were boys. . . ."

When Manabozho was a boy, he lived with his grandmother in a tepee on the edge of the prairies. After the fire had died down at night, the boy would ask about his family.

The grandmother didn't like to talk about them. She would only say that Manabozho's mother was dead and that his father had gone to the land of the setting sun. The boy's three older brothers had gone off, too.

"Long before you were born," the old woman said, "your father gave them their inheritance. He gave to one, power over the South Wind; to another, power over the Wind of the North. Your third brother rules the East Wind."

"What is my share?" asked Manabozho.

But the old woman would say no more. She would watch the fire die until there was only a curl of smoke, thin as a feather, going up to the hole in the roof. Then she would spread her mats of sweetgrass on the platform along the side of the house. She would lie down and go to sleep.

Manabozho had always been large for his age. Now, he began to grow so fast that his grandmother's tepee was no longer big

tepee
(tē ' pē)
tent of the North American Plains Indians; made of skins

inheritance
(in her' ə təns)
something received from one's ancestors

enough to hold him. He had to leave the shelter of the house and live out of doors.

Here, he got to know animals and birds of every kind. He made friends with the thunder, with the clouds, and with the shades of light and darkness.

Still, he kept growing. He grew so tall he could reach the birds in the top of the highest trees. When he hunted he would come back with a deer or a bear under each arm. He could wade out to the center of the lake. There he would catch fish so large that the fat and oil would last his grandmother all winter.

The old woman was grateful for all the fine food the boy brought home. But even so, she would not answer his questions about his father. Finally, she pointed impatiently to the west. "Go ask him yourself!" she cried.

So Manabozho pulled up a tree to use for a walking stick. He stripped it of its leaves and branches with the palm of his hand. Then he set out for the mountains. Three steps took him from one side of the prairie to the other. He hopped over foothills as if they were pebbles. In no time at all he came to the high mountains.

Seated on the top of the highest mountain was a giant as large as Manabozho himself. He was puffing a pipe whose stem was three yards long. The bowl of the pipe was hollowed from a tree of a hundred rings. When he puffed smoke from his pipe, the top of the mountain disappeared in its cloud.

"There's a man who does nothing on a small scale," Manabozho said to himself. "That must be my father."

Manabozho sat himself down on a nearby peak. He did not say what was on his mind at once. In fact, the two giants spent several days talking about this and that. There was no mention of Manabozho's inheritance. The father did things on such a big scale that it took him a whole day to speak a single sentence. But never did he bring up the subject that filled Manabozho's mind.

When three days of empty talk had gone by, Manabozho's feelings changed. He saw that he would have to act. He asked, "What do you fear most on earth?"

"Nothing!" shouted the father. He was so surprised at his son's question that he jerked the pipe out of his mouth. His arm moved and caused a landslide of huge rocks.

"Is there nothing that could hurt you?" Manabozho asked.

The father sighed and three hemlocks fell over from the force of his breath. "Yes, there is a kind of black stone a couple of hundred miles from here. If it should happen to hit me on any part of my body it would hurt me very much. You'll not mention this to anyone, will you?"

hemlocks
(hem' loks)
types of
evergreen trees

Manabozho agreed.

"Now, tell me, my son, is there something *you* fear?"

"Nothing," answered Manabozho, in a voice so fierce that the sun blinked.

"There must be something," the father insisted.

"Well, I will tell you . . . " Manabozho stopped. The words would not come.

"Out with it!" roared the father, hitting his son so hard that the mountain echoed.

"If you must know," Manabozho answered, "I fear the root of the bulrush."

After this, no word was spoken for the rest of the day.

When night came, Manabozho got up and stretched. "I need exercise," he said. "I will step over and get some of the black rock. I just want to see what it looks like."

When he had gone, the father muttered to himself, "I will get a little of the bulrush to learn how it tastes."

At the break of day, Manabozho returned. He had twenty loads of black stone. His father arrived with a whole meadow of bulrushes.

Manabozho was the first to strike. The black rock struck the father between the eyes.

The father returned with a blow of bulrush. It hung over the shoulders of Manabozho like the lightning among clouds.

bulrush
(bul' rush')
a tall, slender
plant that grows
in wet places

meadow
(med' ō)
a piece of grassy
land

14

Back and forth the blows went, but neither of the giants was to be defeated.

"Hold, my son," the father said. "We cannot defeat each other. Stop where you are and I will give you as much power as your brothers have."

"But the four quarters of the earth are already taken!" Manabozho cried. "My brothers have power over the East and North and South Winds and you keep the West for yourself. What is left for me?" And he raised the last black stone, threateningly.

"It is true that the four corners are taken,"

his father said. "But you can do a great deal of good for the people of the earth. You can help the people of the Algonquian country. Their land is full of beasts and monsters of all sorts. If you put forth half the strength you have shown today, you can make a name that will last forever."

So Manabozho forgave his father and accepted power over the Algonquian country. The boy went home to his grandmother to be cured of his wounds.

The young giant had not been home long when he heard of a terrible Manitou living on the side of the Tar Lake. The wicked Manitou refused to allow the people to fish in the lake. He placed two serpents at the entrance to destroy anyone who tried to come through the narrow passage. And he spread tar on the waters to catch any canoe that might slip through.

Manabozho decided it was time to fight the Manitou. Armed with a huge bow and many arrows, the young giant set out in his canoe. In the bottom of the canoe he had placed a jar of oil. He had no use for a paddle. He could send the boat in any direction by the sound of his voice.

The terrible Manitou watched Manabozho's canoe coming closer. He was not afraid. He trusted the two serpents to guard the lake. From his house on the high cliff, he could see

Manitou
(man' ə tü)
an evil spirit
having great
powers

serpents
(ser' pəntz)
snakes

the serpents blowing flame from their mouths. The flames would close the entrance to the lake completely. And that would be the end of Manabozho's loud brags that he would free the lake for fishing. And even if the giant could pass through the entrance, his canoe would stick in the tar that covered the waters.

The two serpents curved their long necks and sent out showers of fire. "We know you, Manabozho," they hissed. "You shall not pass."

Manabozho looked afraid. He turned his canoe around as if beaten. Then he called out, softly, "What is that behind you?"

The two serpents turned their heads. In an instant, Manabozho had shot both of them through their necks with a single arrow.

The entrance now was clear. Manabozho rubbed his canoe from bow to stern with oil. Protected by the oil, the canoe shot through the tar as through a cloud of mist.

The terrible Manitou saw that Manabozho's canoe was almost upon him.

The smoke from the flames sent out by the dying serpents clouded the sky. Manabozho was yelling orders as if he had an army of war canoes behind him. A whole forest of arrows shot through the air.

The Manitou replied with thunderbolts. The battle was on!

bow
(bou)
the front part of a boat

stern
(stėrn)
the back part of a boat

The stone-tipped arrows and the thunder-bolts rattled like hail. In their long houses on the shore of the lake, the Algonquians heard and trembled.

All day the fight raged. When he ran out of thunderbolts, the terrible Manitou reached out his long arms. He beat the young giant with his bare hands.

Manabozho was in despair. How could he take care of these people if he could not rid their lake of this monster?

When it seemed that all was lost, a wood-pecker flew across the lake from the West. It settled on the canoe. "Your enemy has a weak point," the bird said. "Shoot at the lock of hair on the crown of his head."

The first arrow aimed at the Manitou's weak spot drew a few drops of blood. Another arrow brought the Manitou to his knees. Manabozho let fly a third arrow and the monster fell into the lake and was drowned.

The enemy was dead! The Algonquians were free to fish in the lake, even past the serpent's rock.

And Manabozho? Before he left the Tar Lake for further adventures, he rubbed the woodpecker's head with drops of the Manitou's blood. To this day, the bird has red feathers to signify his courage.

Why the Woodpecker Has a Red Head

Thinking About the Story

1. Why did Manabozho's father do things on a big scale? How long did it take him to speak a sentence? What's the longest sentence you ever said out loud?

2. Why do you think Manabozho and his father fought? In this situation was the fight necessary? Could it have been avoided?

3. Look back in the story to find the words the author uses to describe the following: a curl of smoke, foothills, Manabozho's father, how the bulrushes hung on Manabozho's shoulders. How do the describing words help you understand what is happening?

4. The woodpecker helped Manabozho—but why? Was the woodpecker a friend of Manabozho or of all people?

Doing Things

What did an Algonquian village look like? Books in the library can help give a description. Make a model of the village with members of your class.

Profile:
Marguerite de Angeli

Marguerite de Angeli was born in Lapeer, Michigan. Her father's family was from England and Canada. Her grandfather was the town blacksmith. She remembers "big family gatherings at which there might be as many as forty-five people."

Marguerite found that her family life gave her a lot of material to write about. When her father, Shad, died, it seemed time to put some of his stories into words. He used to tell his children about his boyhood in Michigan. He had told them about his friend, Ash. He and Ash had spent days in the woods where there were still bears and wolves. The boys had once found an Indian skeleton buried in a mound. Marguerite's father also told how he had wanted a dog and a pair of boots

with copper toes. Marguerite remembered this, and in 1938 she wrote *Copper-Toed Boots.*

She has written many other books. One is called *Henner's Lydia.* It is about the Pennsylvania German country. Another is called *The Door in the Wall.* It is about thirteenth-century England.

Marguerite de Angeli is an important writer. She cares about the people she writes about. She draws much of her writing from her own experience. She has a good sense of humor, and knows how to "spin a good yarn."

The following story is taken from the book, *Copper-Toed Boots.* Shad, of course, is her father when he was just a boy.

---

spin a good yarn   to tell a good tale

COPPER-TOED BOOTS

Marguerite de Angeli

The farmers and their wives were coming into town. They brought the last of the winter apples and their butter and eggs to trade for coffee, sugar, and salt. All of these things had to be gotten at the store. Already Neppessing Street was filled with wagons and carriages.

Mr. Strong was just dressing the window when Shad reached the store. He was putting into the window a new line of spring shoes and *boots!* There were men's boots for work and men's dress boots. There were ladies' high buttoned shoes, girls' high buttoned shoes, *and* boys' boots! The pair Shad liked best had copper toes and fancy red leather tops with a star set in! Shad stood admiring them.

"Want a job?" said Mr. Strong. "There's a shipment of groceries comin' in this morning. That is, it's comin' in if Windy doesn't get held up too long talkin' at Pontiac. Get the broom and sweep out, that's a good boy!"

Did he want a job! Maybe he could work enough days to earn those boots! Of course, they cost a lot of money—four dollars. But he could try. He gave Mr. Strong Ma's list, and hurried to get the broom and set to work.

Lon, who drove the delivery wagon, said he would take Ma's groceries right up to the house. He thought that he and Roany, his old horse, had the most important work to do in Lapeer. They were great friends, and well suited to each other. Lon had a limp from a wound received in the war. Roany had something wrong with his knees. Once he began to back up, he just couldn't stop. Shad was afraid that sometime he would get to backing down the bank. Then he might go right into the Flint River, which ran along behind the store. But whenever he mentioned it, Lon said, "Nonsense!"

Before Shad was through sweeping, Windy came with the dray-load of groceries. Mr. Strong asked Shad to help carry in some of the packages. By the time the wagon was unloaded, the store was already filled with customers.

"Take this crock of butter from Mrs. Sullivan, will you, Shad?" called Mr. Strong. "Then weigh up some sugar for her."

Shad had helped in the store once or twice before. So he knew how to weigh things. And the prices were marked on a paper tacked to the wall. He felt almost grown-up by the time he had finished.

Old man Cummins came in. He took so long to buy so little that Mr. Strong couldn't be bothered with him. He called to Shad.

"Shad! Can you wait on Mr. Cummins?"

Shad was so proud to be behind the counter, he was glad to wait on the old man. Mr. Cummins never wore his coat, winter or summer. He always carried it over his arm, as if he expected a sudden change of weather. He spoke in a deep whisper, as if what he had to say was a secret of great importance. He cleared his throat.

"Good morning, sir," he whispered, and Shad began to feel very important, too. "A-hem! Ah—I'd like to do a little business.

Ahem!" He studied a crumpled scrap of paper, shifted the tobacco in his mouth, and went on.

"Ahem! Ah—I'll have four pennies' worth of tea. Ahem!" He waited till Shad had weighed it, and tied it up. It was hard to weigh so small an amount.

Then he said, "Ahem! Ah—six pennies' worth of sugar. Ahem!" Shad scooped a little out of the barrel and weighed it.

Mr. Cummins went on. "A-hem! Ah—six pennies' worth of flour, and a bit of cream of tartar. A-hem!" Shad weighed the flour. Then he put about a teaspoonful of the cream of tartar in a paper sack.

Mr. Cummins studied the crumpled paper again. Then he whispered, "Ahem—Ah!—now I'll have a bit of salt pork. Eight pennies' worth. It must be fresh! And I'll have an egg to my tea." Shad thought he spoke a little like Pa, so he must have come from England, too!

Mr. Cummins continued. "Ahem—Ah—you may add up the account. A-RR-ump!"

Shad figured it up quickly. Arithmetic *was* some good! It came to twenty-seven cents.

Mr. Cummins had only a quarter, which he laid down on the counter.

Then he said:

"Ahem—Ah—I find that I am somewhat short of cash. Will you kindly charge the balance to my account? Thank you!" He gathered up the small package and went out.

Shad wished he could have given him more for his money. But he had little time to think about it. The counter was lined with farmers and their wives, waiting to trade. Shad wondered if he would even get home to dinner! He had been hustling up and down the ladder and running back and forth to the cheese box. Shad's legs began to ache. Ma would probably say it was growing pains.

Finally, there was a lull in the trade. Mr. Strong said, "You'd better get along home now and get your vittles. Here's a quarter!"

Shad went. He felt rich. He was as hungry as a bear and hoped that Ma had something good for dinner. When he turned in the walk, there she stood at the window.

"There is no substitute for hard work."
—Thomas Edison

26

Copper-Toed Boots

Thinking About the Story

1. What did people bring to trade for coffee, sugar, and salt? Why didn't they just buy these things?

2. Mr. Cummins bought small amounts of food. What makes you think so? Do people today buy such small amounts? How much do you think six pennies worth of sugar weighed?

3. Describe the shoes Mr. Strong put in the window. Why do you think there were only boots for men in the window? Why wouldn't men wear *shoes*?

Doing Things

1. Do you think Shad ever got his copper-toed boots? Do you think he continued to work at Mr. Strong's store for the money? Get a copy of the book to find out what happened.

2. Today you can buy anything you need in a supermarket. But not too long ago, people bought different things in separate places. They bought meat from a butcher and bread from the baker. What other kinds of stores were there then?

Old Skills and Crafts

Things To Do: What other old skills and crafts do you know? Make a list of those that are still used today, for example, candle-making.

A barn-raising, 1888, Massillon, Ohio.

Quilting bee.

Making soap, Wisconsin.

A craftsman making household utensils and farm tools, 17th century Cotswold Forge, Greenfield Village, Michigan.

Harvesting grain, Indiana.

Gathering maple sap, Wisconsin.

29

Cornhusking bee, 1876.

Cherry festival time, Michigan.

Harvesting wheat the
modern way with
machinery, Illinois.

An old combine machine, Wisconsin.

Flax-scutching bee.

Pioneer children's game:
Bobbing for apples,
Roscoe Village, Ohio.

ABE LINCOLN GROWING UP

Genevieve Foster

A whole year passed in misery and loneliness. Then Abe's father couldn't stand it any longer. He went back to Kentucky, leaving Abe and Sarah alone with Dennis Hanks. Dennis had come to live in their cabin after Aunt Betsy died.

One dismal December day, Abe sat by the fire. He scratched all the letters he could remember in the ashes, wishing he knew how to read. Every day seemed like a week, waiting for his father to come back. Abe knew why he'd gone, but that didn't make waiting any easier. Dennis had just come in with his gun, bringing a squirrel for dinner. Sarah said she'd cook it and try to make it taste good. Abe said he couldn't eat. He couldn't even swallow.

"What if his pa couldn't find anybody to marry?" he thought. "Or what if he did, and she didn't like them—him and Sarah? What if . . ."

All of a sudden he heard horses' hooves. He ran outside. And, almost before he knew it, she was there. His stepmother, Sarah Bush Lincoln. He saw her first, sitting beside his father on the seat of a big wagon. It was piled so high with furniture that it took four horses to pull it.

On top of the pile sat two girls and a boy. They jumped down as the wagon stopped.

They stood staring at Abe and Sarah in their dirty, ragged clothes. Then the tall, straight woman came and stood beside them.

"These are my children," she said, "John and Sarah and Matilda Johnston." Her voice was warm and friendly. "And I suppose you are Sarah Lincoln? And you," she added slowly, "you must be Abraham."

Abe looked up. Her eyes were as friendly as her voice. She didn't even seem to mind that he was too tall or mind that he was homely. She just smiled, and so Abe smiled, too. From then to the end of his life, this second mother was to be "the best friend he had."

"Wa-al now," she said briskly, stepping into the cabin. "First thing for me to do is to make something for us all to eat. Meantime, you young'uns go out to the horse trough. Take this soft soap and wash up good, all over."

Wash up? thought Abe, all over? in the winter? That was a mighty queer notion. But he did it, and it felt good. It felt good, too, to have a comb run through his gritty black hair. And to put on a clean shirt of the Johnston boy's. And sit down to good, hot food with eight folks around the table to eat it.

After supper, his new mother swept up the dirty cabin. But to be halfway decent, she told

trough
(trôf)
long, narrow container for holding food or water

Abe's father, it would have to have a wood floor and a door and windows. Then he could get some lime over to Gentryville and white-wash the walls. Right away, that night, every-body must help carry in the furniture and unroll the feather beds. Abe heard something bumping in the chest as they set it down.

Next morning, when his stepmother opened it, there were two books. One was the Bible. And the other—he could hardly believe his eyes—the other was his beloved fable book.

It was *Aesop's Fables.*

"Kin you read?" his stepmother asked.

Abe shook his head. "Nor kin I," she added quickly. "But you'd like to learn?" She knew the answer before he gave it. "Then I'll make sure that you git the chance. Soon as there's enough settlers around here, we'll have to start up a school."

The winter Abe was thirteen, a school was started. All the children went for a few months. The others didn't half try, but Abe was different. He went over and over the words in the Speller. He practiced writing everywhere, 'specially on the back of the big, wooden fire shovel.

Dennis got interested and made a pen for him out of a turkey buzzard's quill. He

lime
(līm)
white substance made by burning limestone, shells, or bones

whitewash
(hwīt′ wosh′)
liquid for whitening walls, usually made of lime and water

feather beds
(feŦH′ ər bedz)
soft, warm mattresses filled with goose, duck, or chicken feathers

turkey buzzard's quill
(tėr′ kē buz′ ərdz kwil)
feather with a hard tip pulled from a vulture; used for writing

stirred up some ink and brought back some paper from the store at Gentryville to make into a notebook. In it Abe wrote:

Abraham Lincoln
his hand and pen.
He will be good but
Who knows when.

He was now fourteen. At last he could read and write! All day long, his father had chores for him to do. It was hard, grubby work. But as soon as he could lay down his ax and hoe, he was turning the pages of a book, reading as if he were starved.

Tom Lincoln couldn't understand it. "It'd be different," he'd say, "if he was puny or sickly, so's he couldn't go huntin'. But for a big strappin' feller like Abe to take so to book-learnin' is jes' plain queer."

But the good stepmother understood this boy who was so different from the others. Sometimes, as she was patching or knitting, he'd have her listen to him. He would read a funny story aloud, and they'd laugh over it.

The first book Abe ever owned, he got from the first man he ever worked for. That was Mr. Josiah Crawford, a nearby farmer.

Mr. Crawford was a thin, sour man. He had such a way of hanging onto money that he had more of it than any of his neighbors. He could hire them to work for him.

strappin'
(strap' in)
tall, strong, and
healthy

36

Tom Lincoln helped build him a new farmhouse. Then he sent young Abe over to work as a hired man. Abe was fifteen, but close to six feet tall, and strong as he was tall.

One day, Mr. Crawford and two or three other men were puzzling over how to lift a heavy log chicken coop that he wanted moved.

"Whar's Abe?" he cried in his thin, sour voice. "Off readin' again?"

"Mebbe," said one of the men, "or mebbe down by the road, talking to a stranger. You know Abe—can't let a traveler get by without findin' out all he knows."

Just then, the big boy sauntered up.

"Movin' the coop?" he drawled. "Whar to?"

The men pointed. Abe stooped down and hoisted it onto his back. He carried it over and set it down, all by himself. The men were dumbfounded.

Oh, Abe was strong, no doubt of that, agreed his employer. But he was lazy. He could husk corn and chop down trees. He could split rails faster than any two men, if he took a notion. But he'd rather read than work.

Josiah himself didn't care much about books, but he owned a few. He let Abe take one home, warning him to be careful of it. It was a biography of George Washington.

chicken coop
(chik' ən küp)
small cage or
pen for chickens

split rails
(split rālz)
split logs of
wood into
thinner bars,
often used for
fences

banked the fire
(bangkd)
covered the fire
with ashes so
that it will burn
slowly

loft
(lôft)
platform under
the roof for
sleeping

grub
(grub)
to dig up out of
the ground

Abe could hardly wait to start it, and then he couldn't bear to stop. He read all evening until his father banked the fire with ashes and made him go to bed. Abe slept in the loft. To have the book handy as soon as it grew light, he carried it up with him. He laid it carefully between the logs. Next morning when he reached for it, his heart sank. It was soaking wet. There had been rain in the night. What could he do or say?

"Wa-al," said Josiah Crawford, shrewdly. "Seein' it's you, Abe. . . . You put in three days huskin' corn, and you kin keep it."

Only three days! Abe could hardly believe it. When those three days were over, the book belonged to him. It was the story of George Washington's life. He read it again and again. Each time it stirred him with ambition.

"I'm not always goin' to grub and shuck corn and split rails for a livin'," he said to Mrs. Crawford, one morning.

"I'm going to study and be ready for whatever chance may come."

"I do the very best I know how—the very best I can."

—Abraham Lincoln

Dance at Grandpa's

Laura Ingalls Wilder

Laura Ingalls Wilder was born in 1867 in a little log cabin. It was on the edge of the Big Woods, near Pipin, Wisconsin. She lived every event described in her Little House *books. They include* Little House in the Big Woods *and* Little House on the Prairie.

The following story is taken from Little House in the Big Woods. *It takes place at the home of Laura's grandparents. There has just been a "sugar snow." As Pa says,*

"It's called a sugar snow, because a snow this time of year means that men can make more sugar. You see, this little cold spell and the snow will hold back the leafing of the trees, and that makes a longer run of sap."

So off they went to Grandpa's house to help turn the sap into sugar, and to have a big party.

sap
(sap)
life-giving juice
of a plant

In the kitchen Grandma was all by herself, stirring the boiling syrup in the big brass kettle. She stirred in time to the music. By the back door was a pail of clean snow, and sometimes Grandma took a spoonful of syrup from

the kettle and poured it on some of the snow in a saucer.

Laura watched the dancers again. Pa was playing "The Irish Washerwoman" now. He called:

"Doe see, ladies, doe see doe,
Come down heavy on your heel and toe!"

Laura could not keep her feet still. Uncle George looked at her and laughed. Then he caught her by the hand and did a little dance with her, in the corner. She liked Uncle George.

Everybody was laughing, over by the kitchen door. They were dragging Grandma in from the kitchen. Grandma's dress was beautiful, too; a dark blue calico with autumn-colored leaves scattered over it. Her cheeks were pink from laughing, and she was shaking her head. The wooden spoon was in her hand.

"I can't leave the syrup," she said.

But Pa began to play "The Arkansas Traveler," and everybody began to clap in time to the music. So Grandma bowed to them all and did a few steps by herself. She could dance as prettily as any of them. The clapping almost drowned the music of Pa's fiddle.

Suddenly Uncle George did a pigeon wing,

calico
(kal' ə kō)
cotton cloth
printed with
colored patterns

pigeon wing
(pij' ən wing)
dance step

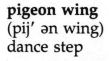

and bowing low before Grandma he began to jig. Grandma tossed her spoon to somebody. She put her hands on her hips and faced Uncle George, and everybody shouted. Grandma was jigging.

Laura clapped her hands in time to the music, with all the other clapping hands. The fiddle sang as it had never sung before. Grandma's eyes were snapping and her cheeks were red, and underneath her skirt her heels were clicking as fast as the thumping of Uncle George's boots.

jig
(jig)
doing a lively dance

fiddle
(fid' l)
violin

Everybody was excited. Uncle George kept on jigging and Grandma kept on facing him, jigging too. The fiddle did not stop. Uncle George began to breathe loudly, and he wiped sweat off his forehead. Grandma's eyes twinkled.

"You can't beat her, George!" somebody shouted.

Uncle George jigged faster. He jigged twice as fast as he had been jigging. So did Grandma. Everybody cheered again. All the women were laughing and clapping their hands, and all the men were teasing George. George did not care, but he did not have breath enough to laugh. He was jigging.

Pa's blue eyes were snapping and sparking. He was standing up, watching George and Grandma, and the bow danced over the fiddle strings. Laura jumped up and down and squealed and clapped her hands.

Grandma kept on jigging. Her hands were on her hips and her chin was up and she was smiling. George kept on jigging, but his boots did not thump as loudly as they had thumped at first. Grandma's heels kept on clickety-clacking gaily. A drop of sweat dripped off George's forehead and shone on his cheek.

All at once he threw up both arms and gasped, "I'm beat!" He stopped jigging.

Everybody made a terrific noise, shouting and yelling and stamping, cheering Grandma. Grandma jigged just a little minute more, then she stopped. She laughed in gasps. Her eyes sparkled just like Pa's when he laughed. George was laughing, too, and wiping his forehead on his sleeve.

Suddenly Grandma stopped laughing. She turned and ran as fast as she could into the kitchen. The fiddle had stopped playing. All the women were talking at once and all the men teasing George, but everybody was still for a minute, when Grandma left.

Then she came to the door between the kitchen and the big room, and said:

"The syrup is waxing. Come and help yourselves."

Then everybody began to talk and laugh again. They all hurried to the kitchen for plates and outdoors to fill the plates with snow. The kitchen door was open and the cold air came in.

Outdoors the stars were frosty in the sky and the air nipped Laura's cheeks and nose. Her breath was like smoke.

She and the other Laura, and all the other children, scooped up clean snow with their plates. Then they went back into the crowded kitchen.

waxing
(waks' ing)
becoming firm,
like wax

Grandma stood by the brass kettle and with the big wooden spoon she poured hot syrup on each plate of snow. It cooled into soft candy, and as fast as it cooled they ate it.

They could eat all they wanted, for maple sugar never hurt anybody. There was plenty of syrup in the kettle, and plenty of snow outdoors. As soon as they ate one plateful, they filled their plates with snow again, and Grandma poured more maple syrup on it.

When they had eaten the soft maple candy until they could eat no more of it, then they helped themselves from the long table loaded with pumpkin pies, dried berry pies, cookies, and cakes. There was salt-rising bread, too, and cold boiled pork and pickles. Oo, how sour the pickles were!

They all ate till they could hold no more, and then they began to dance again. But Grandma watched the syrup in the kettle. Many times she took a little of it out into a saucer, and stirred it round and round. Then she shook her head and poured the syrup back into the kettle.

The other room was loud and merry with the music of the fiddle and the noise of the dancing.

At last, as Grandma stirred, the syrup in the saucer turned into little grains like sand, and Grandma called:

salt-rising bread
bread raised by a portion of the dough kept from a previous baking

44

"Quick, girls! It's graining!"

Aunt Ruby and Aunt Docia and Ma left the dance and came running. They set out pans, big pans and little pans, and as fast as Grandma filled them with syrup they set out more. They set the filled ones away, to cool into maple sugar.

Then Grandma said:

"Now bring the patty-pans for the children."

There was a patty-pan, or at least a broken cup or a saucer, for every little girl and boy. They all watched anxiously while Grandma ladled out the syrup. Perhaps there would not be enough. Then somebody would have to be unselfish and polite.

There was just enough syrup to go around. The last scrapings of the brass kettle exactly filled the very last patty-pan. Nobody was left out.

The fiddling and the dancing went on and on. Laura and the other Laura stood around and watched the dancers. Then they sat down on the floor in a corner and watched. The dancing was so pretty and the music so gay that Laura knew she could never grow tired of it.

All the beautiful skirts went swirling by, the boots went stamping, and the fiddle kept on singing gaily.

graining
(grān' ing)
stage in turning maple syrup to sugar when it starts to separate and turn hard

patty-pans
(pat' ē panz)
little pans used by children to bake small pies and cakes in

Then Laura woke up, and she was lying across the foot of Grandma's bed. It was morning. Ma and Grandma and Baby Carrie were in the bed. Pa and Grandpa were sleeping rolled up in blankets on the floor by the fireplace. Mary was nowhere in sight; she was sleeping with Aunt Docia and Aunt Ruby in their bed.

Soon everybody was getting up. There were pancakes and maple sugar for breakfast, and then Pa brought the horses and sled to the door.

He helped Ma and Carrie in, while Grandpa picked up Mary and Uncle George picked up Laura, and they tossed them over the edge of the sled into the straw. Pa tucked in the robes around them, and Grandpa and Grandma and Uncle George stood calling, "Good-bye! Good-bye!" as they rode away into the Big Woods, going home.

The sun was warm, and the trotting horses threw up bits of muddy snow with their hoofs. Behind the sled Laura could see their footprints, and every footprint had gone through the thin snow into the mud.

"Before night," Pa said, "we'll see the last of the sugar snow."

Dance at Grandpa's

Thinking About the Story

1. What was one source of sugar that the people in this story had? How did Grandma test the syrup? What did the maple syrup turn into after it was graining?

2. What kind of person do you think Grandma was? Find and read the passage that tells what happened when she stopped jigging. Why was everyone quiet?

Doing Things

1. How is maple sap taken from the trees? Find out more about maple sap from books in your library. Give a report to your class about the different things made from it.

2. The words of a square dance tell the dancers what to do next. Practice calling the dance until you "get good" at it. Maybe you'd like to find other dance calls to give or to make up your own directions for a square dance. Then "call them out" to the class. See if people can follow your directions!

Some Pioneer Customs

Pie was usually a part of every meal.

Recipe for snow bread: Take a quart of fresh cornmeal and two quarts of fine drifting snow. Pour the mixture into a large pan and pop into the oven. It bakes a golden brown—and it's delicious if you like baked cornmeal.

Although matches had been invented, the settlers on the frontiers rarely used them. Instead, they kept their fireplaces burning continually. They lit candles and pipes with a burning stick from the fire. If the fire went out, someone went to a neighbor's house to get some live coals for restarting the fire.

There were no stamps or envelopes. Letters were folded and sealed with wafers (small adhesive paper discs). Postage could be paid either before or after the letter was mailed. If the fee was large, the sender often let the receiver foot the bill.

Nearly everything was homemade, even shoes. Children often went barefoot from spring until the first frost. When their feet got cold, these children shooed cows from where they were lying. Then they would stand in that warm spot to warm their feet.

Children used corn cobs left from corn shelling to make cob houses. They put the houses in the fireplace to watch them burn.

---

foot the bill to pay for something

shelling (shel' ing) taking the shells off

cob houses (kob) little houses made from corn cobs by pioneer children

Quilting bees and apple bees were ways that work could be shared with friends. At a "bee," neighbors pitched in to help one another finish a quilt or pick apples or shell corn. Everyone had a "good ol' time" because when the work was done, there always was lots of food and games.

Wood chopping, corn husking, and sheep shearing were also good reasons for neighborly get-togethers. So, too, were wood gathering, carpet rug cutting, geese-plucking, corn planting, house raising, and log rolling.

Most weddings took place at the bride's home; then the couple walked to the groom's home.

Neighbors often celebrated the wedding with a shivaree. This was a French tradition. Slipping up around the newlywed's house at night, the neighbors suddenly set up a loud racket by ringing cow-bells, beating drums, and clank-ing pots and pans. The celebra-tion ended with plenty of good food and merrymaking.

Sometimes, as a practical joke, the groom was carried off into the woods and tied snugly to a tree. He was left there to get loose and get home as best he could.

The bride was sometimes wheeled away in a wheelbarrow and given a rough, wild ride across the countryside.

Little Orphant Annie

Little Orphant Annie says,
   when the blaze is blue,
An' the lamp-wick sputters,
   an' the wind goes woo-oo!
An' you hear the crickets quit,
   an' the moon is gray,
An' the lightnin' bugs in dew
   is all squenched away,—
You better mind yer parents, and yer teachers
   fond an' dear,
An' churish them 'at loves you,
   an' dry the orphant's tear,
An' he'p the pore an' needy ones
   'at clusters all about,
Er the Gobble-uns'll git you
        Ef you
           Don't
             Watch
               Out!

James Whitcomb Riley

LITTLE BEAR

collected by
Jean Cothran

Once an old man and woman had three daughters and the youngest was a little bear.

The two older daughters set out one day to seek their fortunes. After traveling for a while, they looked around and saw the little bear coming closer. They did not want the company of their younger sister. So they took her home and tied her to the doorposts of the wigwam. Then off they went again.

Soon a moving branch warned them that the little bear was following. Here she came with the doorposts of the wigwam on her back. The older sisters untied the posts and tied her to a huge rock. Then they continued on their journey.

But, here came the little bear with the huge rock on her shoulders. The older sisters loosened the rock and threw it into the middle of the river.

This time they took the little bear with them.

After a long journey, they came to a wigwam where a wicked old woman lived. The

wigwam
(wig′ wom)
hut of poles
covered with
birchbark

52

old woman asked where they were going. To seek their fortunes, they answered. She invited them in and gave them supper. The two older sisters then went to sleep.

But the little bear chose to sit by the fire telling stories to the old woman. At last the little bear seemed to fall asleep. Through her eyelashes, the little bear watched the old woman take a long knife from its cover and start polishing it. Just then, the little bear sneezed. The old woman quickly put away her knife. The little bear pretended to go back to sleep.

The old woman moved nearer the fire and dozed off. This was the chance the little bear wanted. On tiptoe, she woke her sisters and they fled from the wigwam.

In the morning when the old woman saw that her three guests had left, she was very angry. She jumped up into the sky and tore down the sun. Hiding it in her wigwam, she hoped the little bear and her sisters would get lost in the dark.

But they kept going and soon came to a large village where all of the men were searching for the sun. Their chief was sick because the sun had disappeared, and the days were cold and dark.

When the chief was told about the three sisters, he knew that the little bear must be someone special. So the chief asked the little

bear whether she could bring back the sun.

"Yes," she answered. "Give me one handful of maple sugar and your oldest son."

Taking the maple sugar, she went to the wigwam of the wicked old woman. The little bear climbed to the top of the wigwam. She tossed the sugar through a hole into a pot of wild rice, which the old woman was cooking. When the old woman tasted the rice, she found it too sweet. So she went out after water to put in the kettle. This was the chance the little bear wanted. She jumped down, ran into the wigwam, grabbed the sun, and threw it back into the sky.

Then she returned to the village and gave the chief's oldest son to her oldest sister for a husband.

The old woman was angry, very angry, to see the sun again in the sky. She jumped up and tore down the moon.

The good chief again became sick because the nights were so dark. He asked the little bear whether she could bring back the moon.

"Yes," she said. "Give me two handfuls of salt and your next oldest son."

Taking the salt, she climbed on top of the wicked old woman's wigwam and dropped it into her pot of wild rice. When the old woman tasted the rice, she found it too salty. So she went out for water to put in the kettle.

This was the chance the little bear wanted. She ran into the wigwam, grabbed the moon, and threw it back into the sky. Then she returned to the village and gave the chief's second son to her second sister for a husband.

The old woman was angry, very angry, to see the moon again in the sky. So she jumped up and tore down the North Star. The good chief became sick at heart because his trappers and rice gatherers had no star to guide them. He asked the little bear if she could bring back the North Star.

"Yes," she said. "Give me three handfuls of bear grease and your youngest son."

Taking the bear grease, she climbed to the top of the wicked old woman's wigwam and

North Star
(nôrth stär)
bright star almost directly above the North Pole

bear grease
(bar grēs)
soft fat from a bear, used to cook with

dropped it into her pot of wild rice. When the old woman tasted the rice, it was too greasy. So she went outside for water to put in the kettle.

This was the chance the little bear wanted. She ran into the wigwam, grabbed the North Star, and tossed it back into the sky.

When the little bear returned, the good chief gave her his youngest son for a husband. And they were married.

But the young man was not happy about having married a bear.

That night the little bear told her husband to throw her into the fire. He didn't want to, but, like his father, he knew she was someone special. He did as she asked. He threw the little bear into the fire. He was amazed to see the little bear change into a beautiful young woman.

The wicked spell that had been placed on her had been broken. After that, the chief's youngest son lived with his bride for fifty gentle winters and fifty-one golden summers. And all of her life he called her "Little Bear."

Rainbow at night,
Shepherd's delight;
Rainbow in morning,
Shepherds take warning.

Little Bear

Thinking About the Story

1. Why didn't the older sisters want Little Bear to go with them? How do you think their feelings about her changed as she helped them?

2. Why was Little Bear so special? Can a person be special even if others don't know it?

3. How does this story remind you of a fairy tale? What other stories can you think of in which animals change to humans?

Doing Things

1. Develop your storytelling skills! Change Little Bear to a different animal. Then make up your own story. You can decide what happens based on what kind of animal you choose.

2. In the story, the wicked old woman was cooking wild rice. Wild rice was an important crop to the Ojibwa Indians. Find out as much as you can about wild rice and report the information to your class.

Chicago Burns

Sonia Fox

The most famous cow in history is probably Mrs. O'Leary's cow. It is said that she had something to do with the start of the Chicago Fire.

No one knows exactly how the fire began. We do know that it started in Mrs. O'Leary's cow barn. The barn was on De Koven Street, on the West Side of Chicago.

One story is that it started on Sunday evening, October 8, 1871. It was about nine o'clock. Someone went into Mrs. O'Leary's barn to milk one of the cows. Somehow the cow kicked over a small lamp. The dry hay in the barn was set on fire. Maybe that is what happened.

Once the dry hay was on fire, the flames spread out of the barn. The strong wind sent burning pieces of wood from Mrs. O'Leary's barn onto other houses and barns.

The watchman at the Little Giant Fire Company was in the watchtower on that Sunday. At about 9:15 P.M. he saw flames that were six blocks south of the station house. He rang the alarm.

The men of the Little Giant Fire Company rushed to the fire.

But other fire companies in the area were given the wrong signal. They did not arrive until the fire was way out of control.

The Little Giant Fire Company could not stop the fire on De Koven Street. The flames spread quickly. The wind was blowing from the southwest. Burning pieces of wood flew in the air, ahead of the big fire. Many small fires were started by those burning pieces that were flying through the air.

By ten o'clock that night, the fire had spread northeast to downtown Chicago. The wind was blowing hard, and there were flames 100 feet high. Even so,

people felt sure the fire would stop at the Chicago River.

But the fire did not stop. By midnight the whole downtown section was burning. Roswell B. Mason, the mayor of Chicago, rushed to City Hall. He sent telegrams to other cities, asking for their help. Fire engines were loaded on railroad cars heading for Chicago. They came from Milwaukee, St. Louis, and Cincinnati.

Flames were everywhere. The new downtown was being destroyed. Even the fire engines caught on fire. Soon there was no more Chicago Fire Department.

The Tribune Building was the last building on the downtown street to burn. Joseph Medill was the publisher of the Tribune. He worked hard with his men to save the building. He wanted to get out a newspaper ahead of the other papers in Chicago.

They worked all through the night. At 7 A.M. on Monday they had to give up their fight against the fire. Later Joseph Medill said, ". . . the 'Tribune' building resembled a volcano."

By 1:30 Monday morning the courthouse was burning. At two o'clock the huge bell was heard ringing as it fell.

About the same time on the

North Side, some trains filled with kerosene burst into flames. This was the oldest part of the city, and it burned rapidly.

Soon all of the water in the city's water tower was used up. Firemen then pumped water from the Chicago River.

Later Monday morning the lumber mills along the river caught fire. People fled to the lake to get away from the heat.

John Mills Van Osdel was the architect who had built the new Palmer House Hotel. He was there. About 9 A.M. he saw the flames heading toward the hotel. He went down to the basement and dug a big hole for all of his plans and record books. Then he covered them with two feet of sand and a thick layer of damp clay. That saved the papers from the fire. John Mills Van Osdel's idea led to the use of clay tile for fireproofing.

At 11 A.M. on Monday the last row of buildings on the south side of the river started to burn. The houses were on Michigan Avenue between Congress and Van Buren Streets. The section was called Terrace Row, and the houses burned quickly.

Monday afternoon the fire in the business section burned itself out. But the fire still burned on the North Side. Only two houses survived.

One was Mahlon D. Ogden's big home, which was almost all wood. It was just north of Washington Square. Mr. Ogden and his friends covered the roof and sides of his house with wet blankets and carpets. Men swept sparks off the roof with buckets of water and brooms. In that way they saved the house.

The other home on the North Side that was not burned was Richard Bellinger's. He and his brother-in-law, both policemen, fought the flames and won. They raked leaves and burned them in piles, so they would not spread the fire. They also burned the wooden sidewalks, fences, and front steps to his house. They kept the roof wet. First, they used water.

---

kerosene (ker′ə sēn) thin oil used in lamps and stoves

Then, they poured all of Richard Bellinger's apple cider over the roof and walls.

Thousands of people had rushed away from the fire to the shores of Lake Michigan for safety. They also ran to Lincoln Park on the North Side. Rich and poor, young and old! Age or money did not make a difference. Everybody was affected. In the rush to escape, many people threw on clothes to cover their pajamas. Each family had brought what they could carry. What they couldn't bring along with them, they buried.

The heat from the fire was great, even at the lake. To keep cool, many people were "buried" in the sand with air holes for breathing. Water was splashed on their sand-covered bodies. People stood in the water with handkerchiefs over their faces. Other people drove their wagons into the lake as far their horses would go. Then they sat and waited.

A cold rain began to fall Monday night, and the fire finally died out between 2 and 4 on Tuesday morning.

It had all begun in Mrs. O'Leary's cow barn. But strange as it may be, her house and barn were left in good condition!

The Peshtigo Fire

In 1871, Wisconsin was struck by the worst natural disaster in its history. This was the great Peshtigo forest fire. The summer and fall of 1871 were very dry. Many small fires broke out at different places in northeastern Wisconsin. Then, on the night of October 8, northeastern Wisconsin burst into flames. The fire wiped out the town of Peshtigo and several villages. About 800 people were killed. This was about 500 more than the number killed in the Great Chicago Fire that same night. The fire destroyed more than $5 million worth of property.

Highlights of the Great Lakes

Things To Do: What cities in the Great Lakes states would you like to visit? Find these places on a map.

The Robie House at the University of Chicago, designed by Frank Lloyd Wright, Chicago, Illinois.

The Michigan Lumbermen Memorial on the Au Sable River, Michigan.

The Green Bay Packers at Lombardi Field, Green Bay, Wisconsin.

Gorgosaurus, Field Museum of Natural History, Chicago, Illinois.

Lincoln Boyhood National Memorial, Lincoln City, Indiana.

Tulip festival, Holland, Michigan.

Coral display, John G. Shedd Aquarium, Chicago, Illinois.

A Mennonite farming community, Holmes County, Ohio.

Renaissance Center, Joe Louis Arena, Detroit, Michigan.

The start of the Indianapolis 500 Motor Speedway Race, Indianapolis, Indiana.

Devil's Doorway, Devil's
Lake State Park, Wisconsin.

Serpent Mound, Ohio.

Other Places To Visit

Illinois
Museum of Science and Industry,
   Chicago
Oriental Institute Museum, Chicago
Lincoln Home, Springfield
Relic Trolley Museum, Elgin
Hauberg Indian Museum, Rock Island

Indiana
Children's Museum of Indianapolis
Evansville Museum of Arts and Sciences
Howard Steamboat Museum,
   Jeffersonville
Conner Prairie Museum, Noblesville

Michigan
Detroit Historical Museum
Henry Ford Museum, Dearborn
Old Waterworks Building Museum,
   Manistee
National Ski Hall of Fame, Ishpeming
Grand Rapids Public Museum

Ohio
Garfield Monument, Cleveland
Fire Department Museum, Cincinnati
McKinley Memorial, Columbus
Pro Football Hall of Fame, Canton

Wisconsin
Milwaukee County Historical Center
Old World Wisconsin Museum, Eagle
Circus World Museum, Baraboo
Little Norway, Blue Mounds

Ice Man and the Messenger of Springtime

collected by Dee Brown

The Ojibwa Indians form one of the largest tribal groups in North America. They once lived in the forest country around the shore of Lake Superior.

The Ojibwa were great fishers. They also hunted in the forests and gathered wild plants and rice. They used birchbark to cover their wigwams, and to make beautiful bark canoes.

Today, about 150,000 Ojibwa live in Michigan, Wisconsin, and Minnesota. They still harvest most of the wild rice that is eaten in the United States.

The following story is an Ojibwa tale about the coming of springtime.

birchbark
(bėrch' bärk')
bark of a birch
tree

Ice Man was sitting in his birch-bark wigwam by the side of a frozen stream. His fire was almost out. He had grown very old and sad, and his hair was long and white. He was lonely. Day after day, he heard nothing but

66

the howling of winter storms sweeping snow across the land.

One day as his fire was dying, Ice Man saw a young man approaching his wigwam. The boy's cheeks were red and his eyes shone with pleasure. He was smiling. He walked with a light, quick step. Around his forehead was a chain of sweetgrass, and he carried a bunch of flowers in one hand.

"Come in, come in," Ice Man greeted him. "I am happy to see you. Tell me why you came here."

"I am a messenger," replied the young man.

"Ah, then I will tell you of my powers," said Ice Man. "Of the wonders I can perform. Then you shall do the same."

From his medicine bundle, the old man drew out a wonderfully carved pipe. He filled it with sweet-smelling leaves. He lighted it with one of the last coals from his dying fire and blew smoke to the four directions. Then he handed the pipe to the young stranger.

After the pipe ceremony was finished, Ice Man spoke. He said, "When I blow my breath, the streams stand still and the water becomes hard and clear as crystal."

sweetgrass
(swēt′ gras′)
sweet-smelling herb used in Indian ceremonies

medicine bundle
(med′ ə sən bun′dl)
collection of items believed to have magical powers; kept in a pouch made from animal skin

67

"When I breathe," replied the young man,
"flowers spring up all over the land."

"When I shake my long white hair,"
Ice Man declared,
"snow covers the earth.
Leaves turn brown and fall from the trees.
My breath blows them away.
The water birds rise from the lakes
and fly to far-off lands.
The animals hide themselves
from my breath,
and the very ground turns as hard as rock."

The young man smiled.
"When I shake my hair,
warm showers of soft rain
fall upon the earth.
The plants lift themselves with delight.
My breath unlocks the frozen streams.
With my voice I call back the birds.
And wherever I walk in the forests,
their music fills the air."

As he spoke, the sun rose higher in the sky
and a gentle warmth came over the place. Ice
Man sat silent. He listened to a robin and a

bluebird singing on top of his wigwam. Outside, the streams began to trickle. And the fragrance of flowers drifted on the soft spring breeze.

The young man looked at Ice Man and saw tears flooding from his eyes. As the sun warmed the wigwam, the old man became smaller and smaller. Gradually he melted completely away. Nothing remained of his fire. In its place was a small white flower with a pink border, the wild portulaca.

portulaca
(pôr chə lak′ ə)

People would call it Spring Beauty because it is among the first plants to signal the end of winter and the beginning of springtime.

Ice Man and the Messenger of Springtime

Thinking About the Story

1. What season of the year does Ice Man represent? What season does the Messenger represent? Find passages in the story to support your answers.

2. Reread page 67, paragraph 5. What ceremony was performed? Why do you think the story-teller included this event in the story?

3. How do you know that winter was ending? Find the words and read aloud. The story-teller used description to signal the end of winter. Find the description and read it aloud.

4. Why do you think some of the conversation between the two men is written in poetic form?

Doing Things

1. Write your own myth. Explain how summer turns to fall, how night becomes day, or the coming of the new year. Share your myth with members of your class.

2. What did Ice Man and the Messenger of Springtime look like? Draw these two characters.

The Underground Railroad

The "underground railroad" was not a railroad at all. It was a system for helping Negro slaves escape to freedom.

The runaway slaves' lives were in danger. Often they were chased by dogs and by officers. They were chased by slave owners and by people who were paid to hunt runaway Blacks. Until they reached a northern state, the runaways hid out. Even in the North, slaves could be tracked down and brought back by their owners. They were only really free in Canada. They hid in the woods and in barns. They hid in pigpens, in haystacks, and in deserted houses. They hid wherever they could find shelter.

Their only guide was the North Star. Their only goal was to reach freedom.

Sometimes they hid underwater. They held a long hollow reed in their mouths. The top of the reed reached the air above the water. This way, they could breathe. Yet, they remained out of sight until danger passed. Sometimes the male runaways dressed as women to escape. Sometimes they were nailed up in a box and shipped to freedom. Sometimes they were hidden on the underside of a wagon. Or they were hidden in a secret room on a ship.

Slaves were bought and sold like horses or wagons or any piece of household goods. The slave owner was given a "bill of sale" for every slave he bought. This paper showed that the slave was his property. If he decided to sell the slave, he gave the new owner a bill of sale. This showed that the slave now belonged to another. If a slave owner decided to give a slave his or her freedom, he gave the slave a bill of sale. The ex-slave could prove that he or she was free.

Also, another way a slave could get freedom was to flee to a northern state or to Canada, where slavery was illegal.

Most of the work of helping runaways get from one place to another was done by slaves themselves. They had secret ways of giving a runaway food, clothing, and directions. Other people who helped the runaways were Quakers and members of other religious groups, and people who were against slavery.

Harriet Tubman helped about 300 slaves escape. She once had been a slave in Delaware, but she fled to freedom in the North. From that time on she worked to help others. She returned to the South nineteen times to lead people to freedom. Slave owners offered $40,000 for her capture, but she was never caught.

Many women and children were part of the flights to freedom. Like the men, they traveled mostly at night, following the North Star. They hid by day. If caught by the Whites, they would be whipped and taken back to their owners.

The underground railroad was most active in Ohio and Pennsylvania. But by the time of the Civil War, runaways were being helped in every northern state from New England to Kansas. Between 1830 and 1860, about 50,000 slaves fled to freedom.

The Underground Railroad

Thinking About the Story

1. The Underground Railroad was not a railroad, but was like one in many ways. What are some of the ways? Who helped the slaves escape?

2. Why was it better to travel at night? Who chased the slaves as they tried to escape? Where did runaways hide during the day?

3. Why do you think a runaway's "only guide was the North Star"?

4. What do you think a slave could do once he or she gained freedom? Was life going to be easier or harder?

Doing Things

1. Harriet Tubman was a Black woman who helped slaves escape. Find out more about her and the Underground Railroad and report it to your class.

2. Freedom means different things to different people. Think about what freedom means to you. Explain those thoughts in an essay, a poem, or a speech to the class.

Americana in Many Tongues

Because settlers in the frontier states came from many different lands, many different languages were used. How many of these can you read or speak?

> **Key:**
>
> E. English   G. German
> R. Roumanian I. Italian
> F. French   S. Spanish
>   D. Dutch

E. All that glitters is not gold.
  R. *Nu tot ce luce este aur.*
  F. *Tout ce que reluit n'est pas or.*
  G. *Nicht alles was glänzt ist Gold.*
  I. *Oro non è tutto quel che risplende.*
  S. *No es todo oro lo que luce.*
  D. *Het is alles niet goud wat er blinkt.*

E. A rolling stone gathers no moss.
  R. *Pétra care se rostogoleşce d'in locŭ în locŭ, nu prinde muschĭ.*
  F. *Pierre qui roule n'amasse pas mousse.*
  G. *Am rollenden Steine haftet kein Moos.*
  I. *Pietra mossa non fa muschio.*
  S. *Piedra movediza nunca moho cobija.*
  D. *Een tollende Steen neemt geen mos mede.*

E. Do not count your chickens before they are hatched.
  R. *Tómna se numĕră bobociĭ.*
  F. *Ne comptez pas vos pulet avant qu'ils soient eclos.*
  G. *Zähl deine Küchlein nicht bevor sie ausgeschlüpft.*
  I. *Far conto dell'uovo non ancor nato.*
  S. *No vendas la piel del oso antes de haber lo muerto.*
  D. *Hij telt zijne kickens eer de eijers gelegd zijn.*

Hide-and-Seek Chants

One, two, three,
Look out for me,
For my eyes are open
And I can see!

One, two, three,
Look out for me,
I'm going to find you
Wherever you be!

One, two, three,
Look out for me!
I see you
Behind that big tree!

A bushel of wheat
And a bushel of corn,
Here I come
As sure as you're born!

A bushel of wheat
and a bushel of rye,
All in three feet of my base
I spy!

One, two, three,
Look out for me!
I'm coming!

THE WILLOW BASKET

Carol Ryrie Brink

Caddie Woodlawn was a real person. She was the grandmother of the author of this story, Carol Ryrie Brink. Caddie grew up in Wisconsin, where her family settled after leaving New England in the mid-1800s.

Carol Brink was an only child, and her parents died when she was young. By the age of eight, she was living with her grandmother, Caddie. Caddie turned out to be a natural storyteller. All of the stories she told Carol were about her own childhood in pioneer Wisconsin.

When she had children of her own, Carol told them these old stories. Later, she decided to write a book about her people and their backgrounds. The material was all waiting in her own memory.

The following story tells about the early pioneer tradition of barn-raising. It also tells about the tradition of good neighbors who help each other out.

pioneer
(pī′ ə nir′)
person who
settles in a new
part of a country

barn-raising
(bärn′ rāz′ ing)
neighborly get-
together to put
up a barn

78

**"It takes a heap o' livin' in a house
t' make it home."**
—Edgar A. Guest

"They're shiftless—that's what they are!" said Mrs. Woodlawn decidedly.

Shiftless was a terrible word in pioneer Wisconsin. Caddie, Tom, and Warren looked sadly at each other. They had been so happy to see the McCantrys come back! But the father, mother, and four children had returned on foot. They were wheeling all that they owned in a wheelbarrow.

Mr. and Mrs. McCantry and the four children were standing in the road now. They cast wistful glances at the Woodlawns' cozy white house. They were waiting for Tom and Caddie to tell their parents of their old neighbors' return.

"But, Mother," said Caddie, "Emma is so nice, and all they've got left is what they can carry in a wheelbarrow."

"They had just as good a chance here as the rest of us," said Mrs. Woodlawn. "They had a farm, but they sold it for what they could get. They wanted to try for something finer. And now, it seems, they are back with nothing but a wheelbarrow."

"We must not judge people too quickly,

shiftless
(shift′lis)
lazy

79

Harriet," said Mr. Woodlawn mildly, from the doorway.

"Oh, Father, we may ask them in for the night, mayn't we?" begged Caddie.

"Well now," said Mr. Woodlawn, with a wink at Caddie over his wife's smooth dark head. "We'd better let the McCantrys go on to the next farm. The Bunns or the Silbernagles will surely take them in for the night."

Mrs. Woodlawn whirled about with a suspicious look in her eyes. She was just in time to catch her husband's smile and the tail end of his wink.

"Go along with you!" she said, beginning to laugh. "I never meant to let them go without supper and a night's rest. You know that. But I do feel better for having said what I think of them!"

Tom, Caddie, and Warren raced away to invite the McCantrys in to supper and comfortable beds. They were a sad-looking lot as they sat along the roadside, waiting for the help of a kindly neighbor. The bottom of Mrs. McCantry's dress was draggled with mud and dust. The two boys were barefoot. But Mrs. McCantry had a bonnet of the latest fashion, trimmed with purple velvet and pansies. And Pearly, the little girl who was next to the youngest, had a new gold ring.

Emma was the eldest of the four and Caddie's own age. She slipped a warm brown arm

through Caddie's and gave her a squeeze. Emma didn't have gold rings or bonnets with pansies. But she was brown, solid, and comfortable. Caddie liked her best of all. When a bird called out in the meadow, Emma could pucker up her lips and imitate it. Emma looked after the little ones as much as her mother did.

Now Mr. McCantry picked up the handles of the wheelbarrow. Caddie thought that his shoulders looked round and bent. The wheel-

pansies
(pan′ zēz)
multi-colored
flowers

81

patchwork quilts
(pach′wėrk′
kwilts)
blankets made
from pieces of
cloth sewn
together

hoops
(hüps)
circular frames
used to hold out
women's skirts

barrow creaked as he rolled it up the path to the front door. Caddie could see that it held some patchwork quilts and cooking pots. And there was a set of Mrs. McCantry's hoops and a clock which was not running.

"Why don't you wind your clock?" asked Caddie. "I hate to see a clock that doesn't go."

"It's broken," said Emma. "We still carry it around, but it's like most of the rest of our things. It won't work anymore."

"That's too bad," said Caddie, but it gave her an idea.

Mr. and Mrs. Woodlawn met the McCantrys at the front door.

"Well, well," said Mr. Woodlawn heartily, shaking his old neighbor's hand. "So you have come back to us again, McCantry? Dunville is a pretty good place after all."

"It is that!" said Mr. McCantry. "I'm glad to be back. We've been a weary way."

"Now, Josiah, why do you say that?" cried Mrs. McCantry sharply.

Caddie looked at her in surprise. She saw that Mrs. McCantry had lost her sad look of a few moments ago. She was quite the fine lady once again.

"We really have had a most wonderful journey," she said. "We spent some months with my brother. He has a most elegant house which puts anything you have here in Dun-

ville quite to shame. Of course, we were well taken care of. And it is only by the smallest chance that you see us like this. An accident happened to our horse and carriage. We just thought how healthful it would be to come along on foot."

"Yes, yes, of course," said Mrs. Woodlawn. "Now do come in and wash yourselves for supper."

The two little boys went along with Tom and Warren. Pearly was taken in charge by Caddie's little sisters, Hetty and Minnie.

Caddie squeezed Emma's arm.

"Come up to my room," she said.

"Wait," said Emma, smiling mysteriously. "I've got a present for you, Caddie."

"A present for me?" Caddie was amazed.

"It's not very good," said Emma shyly, "but I made it myself. An old lady took us in one night, when we hadn't any money. She showed me how."

She fumbled through the messy bundle of quilts and pots in the wheelbarrow. Then she brought out a little willow basket.

"Why, it's ever so pretty!" cried Caddie, really pleased. "But you ought to keep it for yourself."

"Oh, I can make lots more of them," said Emma. "Big ones, too; but we don't have room to carry them. I thought you'd like this little one."

willow
(wil′ō)
tree or bush
whose branches
bend easily

83

smokehouse
(smōk' hous')
building in
which meat or
fish is treated
with smoke to
keep it from
spoiling

smoked
(smōkt)
treated with
smoke

"I'd love it," said Caddie. "Thank you, Emma."

Meals were always good at the Woodlawns'. But any sort of company drove Mrs. Woodlawn to extra effort. Tonight she went to the smokehouse and took down one of the hams. It had come from one of their well-fed pigs. And it had been salted and smoked under her own direction.

With a sharp knife she cut the tender pink slices. Then she fried them to a light brown before heaping them on the big blue china platter. Each slice was half-ringed with a small layer of fat—just enough to make it taste good.

Mr. Woodlawn filled the plates of the hungry-looking McCantrys. Emma and the smaller boy fell to with a will. But Pearly set up a thin wail of protest.

"I can't eat this," she said, pointing a finger at the fat.

"Me neither," said Ezra, the littlest brother.

"You can't eat that tender bit of fat?" cried Mrs. Woodlawn in surprise.

"They've got touchy stomachs," Mrs. McCantry said proudly.

For a moment Mrs. Woodlawn was speechless.

"Maybe Mama could cut the fat part off for you, Pearly," began Mrs. McCantry.

Mrs. Woodlawn's earrings began to shake as they always did when she was excited.

"No," she said, with that gleam in her eye that her own children had learned to obey. "If you can't eat that good ham just as it is, fat and lean, you're not very hungry. My children eat what is set before them with a relish. They know if they don't, they can go to bed empty. Anyone who eats at my table can do the same."

Caddie saw with twinkling eyes that Pearly and Ezra were eating their fat with their lean. Personally she thought the fat was the best part. She liked it all crisp on the outside and juicy on the inside, like Mother fried it.

The McCantrys were not there for only one night. They stayed on for many days, but there were no more complaints about their meals.

Caddie and Emma enjoyed the time very much. Together they went down to the swamps where the young willows grew thick. The boys helped them cut slender, young shoots to weave more baskets. The Woodlawn land and Dr. Nightingale's land came together here at the edge of the swamp. Beyond their fences the swamp stretched away in a fairyland of tiny hummocks and islands. Miniature firs and tamaracks grew there. There were also wild rice in the swamp in the autumn and lots of wild cranberries.

swamps
(swomps)
wet, soft land

shoots
(shüts)
new parts
growing out;
young branches

hummocks
(hum' əks)
very small
rounded hill

tamaracks
(tam' ə raks)
American larch
trees

reed
(rēd)
tall grass with a
hollow stalk that
grows in wet
places

"What a pretty place this is!" said Emma. "If I were you, Caddie, I would build a little house on this hill overlooking the swamp. I like the nice spicy swamp smell, don't you?"

A red-winged blackbird, swaying on a reed, uttered a throaty call, and Emma answered.

Caddie remembered this later, when she heard her father and mother talking about a home for the McCantrys.

"Really, Harriet," said Mr. Woodlawn, "I've talked alone with McCantry. They have reached rock bottom. He hasn't any money left."

"To hear *her* talk, you would think they were millionaires."

"I know, my dear, but she's a proud woman. It's her pride that's brought them where they are, I think. But we can't let them starve for all that. And we can't have them living with us always, either. Somehow we've got to set them on their feet once more."

"Well, Johnny, grumble as I may, I suppose that you are always right about such things. What should we do?" sighed Mrs. Woodlawn.

"I thought we might give them a little land at the edge of our place somewhere. Perhaps one of our neighbors on the other side would contribute a little, too. Then all of the neighbors could get together and help them build a

86

raising bee
(rāz′ing bē)
a get-together to
help build a barn

site
(sīt)
place

house. We could make a sort of raising bee out of it.''

''A raising bee!'' repeated Mrs. Woodlawn, her eyes beginning to shine. ''Yes, we could do that.''

''Oh, Father,'' cried Caddie. ''That would be lots of fun! And I'll tell you the very place for the house.''

''You will?'' laughed her father. ''So you've already picked the site?''

''Yes, I have! It's that corner down by the swamp. Emma loves the smell and the red-winged blackbirds. They could get all the cranberries and wild rice they needed. And maybe they could sell what they didn't need. They could make willow baskets out of the willow shoots and sell those, too.''

''Willow baskets?'' asked her father. ''Sell willow baskets? You're going a little fast for me, daughter. I'm lost in the swamp.''

''Oh, wait!'' cried Caddie. She was in one of her eager moods when ideas came too fast to be said. She flew out of the room and returned with Emma's basket in her hands.

''Look! Wouldn't you pay money for a big basket, if it were as nicely made as that?''

Her mother took the basket in her own small hands and looked it over carefully.

''Yes, I would,'' she said. ''I believe a lot of people would. We've never had anyone around here who could make baskets.''

"Well, we have now," said Caddie. "Can't we set the McCantrys up in business?"

"Where's my bonnet?" cried Mrs. Woodlawn. "I'm going to call on the neighbors!"

Dancing with excitement, Caddie ran for her mother's gray bonnet.

"At least it doesn't have purple pansies on it," said Mrs. Woodlawn, as she went to the barn for a horse.

There was nothing like another's need to rally the pioneers of that day. Dr. Nightingale joined Mr. Woodlawn in giving a good-sized strip of land at the edge of the swamp. Another man offered enough logs to build a cabin, if others would cut and haul them. Men and boys, who had nothing to give but their time, gladly did the cutting and hauling. One neighbor offered a pig. Another offered a cow. And a third offered the use of his horse and plow to break a garden spot.

On the day of the "raising," men and boys on horseback arrived from all the country around. They went right to work on the cabin. The women and girls came along later in the morning. They brought covered dishes and jars of pickles and preserves.

They had made tables by putting long planks on sawhorses near the site of the new house. Over an open fire were great pots of coffee. And there were stone jars full of Mrs. Woodlawn's baked beans.

rally
(ral′ē)
bring together

preserves
(pri zėrvz′)
fruit cooked with
sugar and sealed
from the air

sawhorses
(sô′ hors iz)
frames for
holding wood
that is being
sawed

hewed
(hyüd)
shaped wood
with a broadax, a
special tool for
hewing

It was not often that the neighbors came together for a common purpose. They were a settled community now. It had been a long time since there had been a "raising" in the neighborhood. They came together in a spirit of friendship and helpfulness.

The children raced about playing tag, "Blindman's Buff," and "I Spy." The men laid up stone for a fireplace. They hewed and raised the logs one upon another to make the McCantrys' walls. The women unpacked baskets and laughed and chattered as they spread the feast. They were seeing friends and neighbors they had not seen for weeks, perhaps for months or years.

There was one thing which Mrs. Woodlawn and Mrs. McCantry had in common. They both loved a party. With happy, flushed faces they moved about among the neighbors. They shook hands and filled coffee cups. They urged more beans or gingerbread on people who had already eaten their fill.

The swamp echoed with the cries of men as they heaved the upper logs into place. By sundown the McCantrys had a house of their own. All the hard work was done and only the finishing was left for Mr. McCantry.

As the neighbors started to leave, other gifts came out of their wagons. There were a sack of potatoes and a rocking chair. Someone gave a bushel of turnips and a goosefeather

bushel
(bush' əl)
measure
containing 32
quarts or 4 pecks

90

pillow. And finally, there were a string of dried apples and a couple of live chickens.

At the last moment, Mr. Woodlawn nailed up a shelf by the new fireplace. No one knew why until Caddie and Emma rushed over the fields from the Woodlawn's house. They were carrying the McCantrys' clock. Caddie and her father had sat up late in the attic shop the night before. They had taken it all apart, cleaned it, and coaxed it to run. Now it ticked away on the shelf as happy as a cricket.

"There!" said Caddie. "A house is ready to live in when a clock is ticking in it!"

"My land!" said Mrs. McCantry. "That clock hasn't ticked for years—just like us, I guess." Her bonnet was all crooked with excitement and the purple pansies bobbed and trembled over one ear. But for once her eyes were perfectly frank and honest. "I know what you've been thinking of us, Mrs. Wood-lawn," she said slowly. "Shiftless, you thought, and I guess you were right. But we've seen what neighbors can be like today. We're going to set right out to be good neighbors ourselves. You won't ever regret all that you've done for us!"

The two women looked at each other and for the first time they smiled in sudden understanding. Caddie and Emma smiled and hugged each other.

The McCantrys would be good neighbors.

cricket
(krik′it)
insect in the grasshopper family

The Willow Basket

Thinking About the Story

1. How did Caddie help the McCantrys? What idea did she have about land for their new house?

2. Compare Mrs. McCantry to Mrs. Woodlawn. Reread page 91, paragraph 3 (starting with "My land"), to the end of the story. How did each woman change at the end?

3. Why is "The Willow Basket" a good title for this story? Do you think Emma could help her family by making baskets and selling them?

Doing Things

1. Parts of "The Willow Basket" would make a good play. Choose a scene such as the dinner table scene on pages 84–85. Then act out the scene for your class.

2. Pioneer women held quilting bees to help each other sew quilts. Hold a quilting bee with members of your class. Use squares of paper that are the same size for your patches. Make a colorful design on your paper patch. Join all of the patches together with tape for a display.

Three Special "Pioneers"

Jane Addams

Jane Addams was a woman who became famous by helping the poor. In 1931, she won the Nobel Peace Prize for all the work that she had done. What had she done?

She founded a place called Hull House. It was a neighborhood center on the southwest side of Chicago. Hull House was a place where immigrants could get help. They could learn the English language, find work, get care for their children, and find friends.

Jane Addams also worked to get laws passed to help working women. She worked to get the first law passed that made it illegal to hire children to work in factories. She led in the fight to give women the right to vote.

Jane Addams—an outstanding woman!

Nobel Peace Prize (nō bel' pēs' prīz') prize named after a Swedish inventor given to people who work to better humanity

Henry Ford

One of the great inventions of this century was the Model T Ford. It was developed by a highly inventive man, Henry Ford.

He began working with engines about 1890. Soon he invented an engine that would propel a "buggy," a horseless carriage. From that early beginning came the Model T Ford. That car and a long list of cars that followed bore his name, Ford.

The first cars were expensive because all the parts were made by hand. Henry Ford figured out how to put a car together on an "assembly line." That lowered the cost. In time, this mass-production method made it possible to sell cars at prices many people could afford.

The first car Henry Ford built, in 1896, still runs. You can see it at the Henry Ford Museum in Dearborn, Michigan.

Henry Ford—a great inventor!

"Money is like an arm or a leg—use it or lose it."
—Henry Ford

mass-production (mas′ prə duk′ shən) made in great numbers

Some Famous Ohioans

Ohio has been called the "Birthplace of Flight and Light." The Wright Brothers, Thomas Edison and Neil Armstrong are some of America's most famous people.

John Deere

John Deere was a blacksmith in Illinois. A lot of farmers came to him to have their horses shod and their wagon wheels mended and their tools sharpened. While they waited for the work to be done, they talked. One thing they talked about most was the trouble they had with their plows. It seemed that many farmers shared this problem.

This set John Deere thinking: How can I design a plow that will do what farmers want it to do?

By 1857, John Deere had designed such a plow and was making about 10,000 of them a year. This was the beginning of a manufacturing company. Today it is one of the largest industrial firms in the United States.

John Deere—a remarkable designer!

blacksmith (blak' smith) person who works with iron

plows (plouz) big tools for cutting the soil and turning it over

industrial firms (in dus' trē əl fėrmz) companies that make items, such as cars or machines, in large amounts

Work and Play on the Great Lakes

Port of Cleveland on Lake Erie, Ohio.

Things To Do: Make up a bulletin board display for the Great Lakes. Divide it into Work and Play sections. Draw or cut out pictures for your display.

A Wisconsin dairy farm.

Chicago skyline.

A self-unloading iron ore carrier in Ashtabula, Ohio.

Ice fishing on Lake Michigan.

Sailing on the Grand Traverse Bay, Michigan.

Unloading grain at a port in Indiana.

Mackinaw Island Reserve, Michigan.

Old ball game played with broom-like equipment at the Rock Cut Winter Carnival, Illinois.

Logging in northern Michigan.

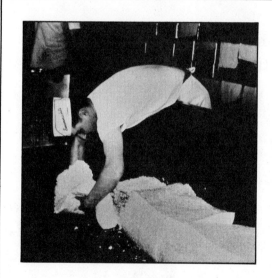

Making cheese in Wisconsin.

Recreational fishing on Lake Michigan.

BRINGING IN THE SHEAVES

Harvey Jacobs

bobwhite
(bob' hwīt')
quail, which is a
kind of bird

harvesting
(här' vist ing)
gathering in food
crops, usually in
the fall

hail
(hāl)
frozen rain

hired hands
(hīrd handz)
people paid to
work and help
out

"Bob White . . . Bob—Bob White . . .
Is your wheat ripe?"

Bobwhites may not have known about harvesting, but they loved our wheat fields. As the wheat ripened, the bobwhites became more numerous.

We waited and watched. We hoped that the rains and hail would not come. A good wheat crop was "money in the bank" for farmers.

Wheat harvesting was an exciting time for us kids. We felt the suspense for days before it started. We liked seeing the big machines moving across the fields. We liked having new hired hands around. We liked the bustle of getting things ready in the kitchen and in the barn and in the field.

One of our Sunday school songs came right out of the wheat field:

Sowing in the morning,
Sowing seeds of kindness,
Sowing in the noontide
*   and the dewy eve;*
Waiting for the harvest
*   and the time of reaping,*
We shall come rejoicing,
Bringing in the sheaves.

sowing
(sō′ing)
planting

The cutting day came with a hot southwest wind. The wind seemed to blow gold into the wheat. The long stand of golden grain swayed and twisted in the wind. It was like an easy dance, rolling and rustling. Then suddenly the dance ended. The wind stopped blowing and the heat settled over us. The ripened grain stood shimmering like a calm ocean in the summer sun. It was waiting, waiting, waiting for someone to come and cut it.

sheaves
(shēvz)
bundles of grain

My father walked into the field. He would pluck a head of wheat and crumble it in the palm of his hand. Gently, he separated the kernels from their tiny husks.

When the grains were free, he poured them from hand to hand. He blew softly on them as they passed between his hands. The chaff drifted out on the breeze, and the wheat

chaff
(chaf)
stiff, straw-like
bits around
grains of wheat

101

remained. After a long time of chewing and testing in different parts of the field, he would say, "It's a little milky yet, but it will be ripe by the time we get things ready."

Then he gave me and the hired man a list of things to do before the cutting began:

"There's a binder to be cleaned and trucked,
And a sickle to be sharpened;
. . . Oil the bundlecarrier,
Sun the canvases;
And don't forget the threader and knotter. . .
Ready the hitches—
Load the twine,
Tell the shockers it's $3 a day and dinner;
Harvey, you will carry water."

The wheat binder was the most complicated piece of machinery we owned. It cut wheat eight feet at a time and rolled the straw over moving canvases through a bundling machine. The binder wrapped a length of twine around each bundle, tying it tightly in the middle. It then kicked out the bundle in less time than it takes to read this sentence.

The binder had two sets of wheels—one for moving from field to field, and another for use during the cutting. "Trucking" the binder

sickle
(sik′əl)
eight-foot bar at the front of a binder with blades that cut off the grain

hitches
(hich′əz)
metals straps used for fastening

102

meant to put it on its traveling wheels. Then it would travel down the road from one farm to another, or from one field to another.

It took a lot of muscle power to work a job on the binder. Most farm kids measured their growth by figuring how long it would be before they could work on the binder.

"Opening up a field" was a special operation. The binder moved around the edge of the field, cutting as close to the fence as possible. The first time around the field left a ragged edge. It was difficult to get close to the fence and into the corners. The second time around the binder was turned around and started back in the opposite direction. The ragged edge was smoothed up, and the cutting proceeded in an almost perfect square. With each time around the field, the square got smaller and smaller. Then at last the cutting ended with the binder being in the center of the field.

As the stalks of wheat were cut, they were gathered up in bundles and tied with a tight cord. The binder ejected the bundles and the shockers began their work. Shockers were those men who stacked the bundles into wigwam-shaped piles.

stalks
(stôkz)
the stems of a plant

103

My grandfather said you could tell what kind of worker a man was by the way he shocked wheat. If he came dawdling up with his bundle to lean it against what someone else had started, he was a loafer. Good shockers began a shock by setting two bundles together, hard, and with a downward thrust. A man who had shocked wheat all day did not need to be rocked to sleep that night.

After the wheat was cut and shocked, it would be picked up and fed into a threshing machine. It separated the grain from the stalks. The threshing happened after the cutting was all done and the binder had gone off to another field of ripened wheat.

On threshing day, an army of men and machines and kids and carts and horses and mules came to the field. The shocks of wheat were brought from the field into the barnyard. There they were fed into the threshing machine, and out came a stream of grain. A long-necked chute threw the grain into storage bins. And the stalks came out another spout and piled up into a straw stack.

A straw stack was as important as a barn. It helped provide shelter, barn bedding, and food for livestock during the winter.

But the special joy of harvesting came when the grain was taken in horse-drawn wagons, into the village elevators. The elevators were huge silo-like buildings where hundreds of tons of wheat could be stored. Then the wheat would be shipped to the flour mills around the country.

The wheat we sold brought in cash to pay all the farm bills—and sometimes enough more for a new piano or a new Model T Ford, or a trip to see the relatives in Kentucky.

Bringing in the Sheaves

Thinking About the Story

1. Reread page 101, paragraph 1. How does the author describe the ripening wheat? Find and read the words that tell about it. Did the wheat really do a dance?

2. Did each person on the farm have a job to do during the harvest? What could a small child do? a very old person?

3. You may have read weather reports in the newspaper. What do you think an early frost would do to the crops? a hot, dry spell? too much rain, or a flood?

Doing Things

1. Find pictures of farms in magazines. Cut them out and paste them onto paper. Then display them for the class. Talk about the many kinds of farms.

2. Many different kinds of jobs besides planting and harvesting are done on farms today. Read about some of these jobs and hold a class discussion.

WHERE ARE THE COWBOYS, GEORGE?

collected by
Carol Ann
Bales

Katie Thiel came to America from Germany when she was a young woman. She settled in Chicago, Illinois. This is her story, in her own words.

I was working in a hotel in The Hague—it was 1928—when I met George. My sister called me and said, "Katie, I'm going to have a party. Will you come and bring a girl friend? There are two fellows here that need dates." Well, the two fellows were George, who'd come from America, and his cousin from the Dutch East Indies (now called Indonesia).

George and I stuck together that whole evening, and we had a nice time. When they took me to the train to go back to The Hague, what did he do, that quiet man? He began to talk.

"I like you. I want to marry you. Oh, marry me!" He asked if I would like to go to America. America? My goodness, the cowboys are in America!

The Hague
(hāg)
capital of the
Netherlands
(Holland)

**Dutch East
Indies**
(duch' ēst'
in'dēz)
colonies in the
East Indies that
used to belong to
the Dutch

I wanted to marry George. But first I had to ask my mommy. So I wrote to my mommy, and she said, "Katie, you come home right away; I never met that man."

I told George he'd have to go home with me to meet my mother. So we went to Germany to my little hometown, Meppen. My mommy looked at him, and she said, "He's a nice man." So we got together. George is very quiet. I'm just the opposite. We were married in Germany, and George went back to the United States. I came later.

The boat landed in New York. I saw the Statue of Liberty and all the high-rises. I said, "George, is this America? Where are the cowboys?"

high-rises
(hī′ rīz′əz)
tall buildings

> **"We are a nation of many nationalities.
> . . . bound together by a single unity,
> the unity of freedom and equality."**
> —Franklin Delano Roosevelt

It was twenty-seven years later that we finally took a trip west. Then I saw cowboys. See, you get big ideas about cowboys when you're a kid. I thought America was full of cowboys.

We visited my great-uncle's grave in California on that trip. My great-uncle's name was Herman Hoormann. He came to America in about 1840 and went in a covered wagon to San Francisco. He found gold.

He must have been a very wealthy man. I said to George, "I want to go over there once and see where that great-uncle of mine was buried." You should have seen the great big monument! It was as high as the ceiling. Herman Hoormann, born in Meppen, Germany. I stood there and thought, "You should know that your grandniece stands here. She came to America, too."

I forgot to tell you something. Before I came to America, when I was the only child left at home, I went to visit my father in the hospital.

covered wagon
(kuv′ ərd
wag′ ən)
wagon with a
canvas cover that
can be taken off

He said to me, "Katie, take care of Mommy when I'm gone." I said I would do that.

So before we got married, I told George, "You know, I can't go to America because I promised my papa I'd take care of Mama."

"Oh, don't you worry about that," George said. "Your mama can come to visit us in America."

Two years later, Mama was all alone in Europe. Her eight children had all disappeared—one here, one there. And we wrote, "Mama, would you like to come visit us?" She said she'd love it. We sent her a ticket and got her a visa for six months. You know how long she stayed? Nine years.

And if I had it to do over again, I would do it tomorrow. She was so happy here in this country. She had the life of a queen. You know, going out with the women's clubs, having luncheons downtown. She had it nice.

We sent packages to my sister back in Germany every week. She called us her "rich American" relatives. That was her idea of us. But later, she and her husband came to visit us. They found out then that the "rich Americans" didn't find the money in the street. We worked for every penny we earned. We worked for it, and we didn't mind.

Immigrants often had no parents, no brothers and sisters, no children of their own. So

visa
(vē′zə)
permit to visit a
foreign country

immigrant
(im′ə grənt)
person who
comes into a
country to live

110

we had no one to depend on except ourselves and those friends from other countries who were in the same boat.

And you'd be surprised how close-knit those friends got to be in times like that. Almost as close-knit as brothers and sisters. We all had the same troubles. We found help in at least being able to discuss those troubles with somebody. And if the need got too bad in one place, well, you did what you could to help out. You brought them a basket of groceries or paid the rent for a month. Or you found a doctor who didn't charge too much.

George and I went back to Europe for a visit in 1962. After about three months of traveling around, we had stopped in Hamburg, Germany. We were standing by the Elbe River. As a ship passed, the crew raised the flag and played the national anthem of that ship's country. It was an American ship. We were singing the American national anthem. And George stood there, big tears rolling down his cheeks. Me, too.

"It's nice to visit here, George," I said. "But it's not home anymore. Home is now in America."

"The republic is a dream. Nothing happens unless first a dream."

—Carl Sandburg

Some Immigrant Traditions

Many immigrant groups arrived in America between 1840 and 1920. They each brought recipes and tastes for certain foods from their home countries.

The Irish often ate bread, fish, and potatoes. On special occasions they ate corned beef and cabbage. Italians ate bread, potatoes, eggs, fish, and pasta. Russians and East European Jews ate herring and challah, or egg bread. They also drank a lot of tea.

Many immigrant food traditions have stayed with us today. Grandchildren of Italian immigrants still serve zeppole during the holidays. East European Jews still eat hamantashen to celebrate a holiday called Purim. Food is one way people show off the country and traditions they come from.

Crafts are another way. Many Poles, Lithuanians, Ukrainians, and other European-American groups make decorated Easter eggs. They are sometimes called pysanky, from the Ukrainian word *pysaty*, which means "to write." Another special craft is beautiful paper cuttings, made with scissors. The Japanese call it kirigami, the Germans call it scherenschnitte, and the Poles call it wycinanki.

These crafts can still be seen today. They are being done by people who carry on the rich traditions of their ancestors.

---

zeppole (zep′ ō lə) a fried, sweet, doughy cake like a doughnut

hamantashen (hum′ ən tosh′ ən) small cakes, filled with poppy seeds or fruit, shaped to look like a triangular hat

Pone, Cake, Dodger and Mush

The pioneers, like the Indians, grew corn in little rocky gardens as well as in large, well-turned fields. Corn was a basic food. The seed was easily stored through winter weather. Moreover, corn grew well in most climates and in most kinds of soil.

A certain amount of shelled corn was saved from each year's harvest. This corn was used for seed when the next planting season came about.

The first settlers planted corn wherever they found a clear spot. They even planted close to trees when there were no open meadows for planting. They poked a hole in the earth with a stick and dropped in the seeds. Then they covered the "hill of corn" with dirt kicked up by the toe of the boot.

Hungry settlers sometimes ate ears of corn before they were fully grown. They ground up the young ears, cob and all, for making green mush cakes. That certainly wouldn't be like eating corn as it comes today in a can from the grocery store.

In the fall when the corn was hard and ready for picking, the ears were brought to the barn. Later the husks that enclosed the corn were stripped off and thrown aside.

---

mush (mush) cornmeal boiled in water

A husking bee brought the whole neighborhood together to help a settler get the corn crop ready for winter storing. The huskers divided into two teams and the pile of corn to be husked was divided in half. Then the race was on! The team that finished husking its pile first was the winner. The winners received no prizes, but they enjoyed teasing the losers. At the end of the bee, winners and losers alike were treated to a bountiful meal.

Another bee-husking event was the search for ears of corn that contain red kernels. The young man finding a red ear had the right to plant a kiss on the lips of his favorite girl. Of course, this kind of partying got the corn husked in a hurry.

Corn was cooked in many different ways. The hard grains of corn were first pounded into a soft, powdery meal.

Five main dishes were made from the cornmeal. *Dodgers* were doughballs made of cornmeal, water and salt. They were baked in an iron kettle or skillet buried in the hot ashes in a fireplace.

Johnnycakes or *hoecakes* were made like the doughballs. But they were spread out on a flat board and baked before an

---

husking bee (hus'king bē) neighborly get-togethers to take the dry covering off ears of corn

open fire. Sometimes the dough was wrapped in leaves or corn husks and baked in the ashes.

Pone was the richest of the corn dishes. It was made by adding yeast and milk to the cornmeal. Then it was baked in the oven or in a covered kettle in the fireplace.

Mush was easily made by adding the cornmeal slowly to a pot of boiling salted water. It was eaten in a bowl with milk or gravy or bear oil poured over it. If any was left over, it was poured out into a pan to cool and harden. Then it was sliced and fried, to be eaten with maple syrup, molasses, or honey.

Hominy grits were made from the whole kernels of corn. The ker- nels were soaked in lye made from wood-ashes. The hulls loosened and pulled away from the soft inside of the kernel. The white flesh of the kernel was then boiled or fried for eating.

If the corn supply was low, settlers mixed mashed pumpkin with it. That made the corn go farther in feeding a family. Sometimes ground-up corn was roasted or burned in the fire, and used for making a drink something like coffee.

Today everyone is familiar with corn flakes and pops and toasties. For a change, you might ask for a bowl of mush or a johnny-cake. You just might like them better!

F.J. Webb - Teacher.
Rina Gadlin
Bessie Hoffman
Nettie Gadlin
Cora Sheppard
Jennie Hoffman
May Hoffman
Emma Green.
Oscar Grimes.
Lester Green,

Pleasant Rr

Autograph Book Verse

Autograph writing
Is very tough;
Here's my name
And that's enough.

Love many
Trust a few
But always paddle
Your own canoe.

2 Y's U R
2 Y's U B
I C U R
2 Y's 4 me.

Remember M
Remember E
Then you'll be
Remembering ME.

Columbus discovered America
In 1492.
I discovered a real nice friend
When I discovered you.

PAUL BUNYAN INVENTS THE SHIFT SYSTEM

Roberta Strauss Feuerlicht

Paul Bunyan, for many people, is the spirit of the American lumberjack. Stories about him have been written from the Pacific Northwest all the way to Maine.

Unlike real folk heroes such as Mike Fink, Paul Bunyan is a made-up character. His popularity grew out of a <u>written</u> rather than an oral tradition. As time went on, the stories about him grew more and more fantastic.

The following tall tale is about one of Paul's inventions, and why it came to be.

Now Paul Bunyan was one of the kindest bosses in the logging business. He treated his men well. He was proud of the fact that he fed his crews better than any logging boss.

But one day he saw that one of his men was getting pale and scrawny.

"What's wrong, Jim?" Paul wanted to know.

"I'm afraid I haven't been eating much, Paul," said the logger, looking embarrassed.

scrawny
(skrô′nē)
skinny

118

"Why not?" asked Paul. "Isn't the tea strong enough to float an ax? Aren't the pancakes thick and steamy? Don't the sausages snap when you bite into them?"

"I don't know," said the logger. "I haven't eaten any lately. There are just too many men in the cookhouse. There isn't time or place to feed us all. The last time I ate was three weeks ago when I speared a doughnut rolling down the table. And I was so weak I could hardly hold onto it."

Paul was very upset when he heard this. First he took Jim in and fed him from his own plate. Then he called in the cooks, Johnny and Sam. They talked for a while, and it was plain and true. The logger was right. There were just so many men in camp that it was impossible to feed them all at the same time.

So Paul invented the shift system. It is still in use today all over the world.

In Paul's camp it worked this way. He divided the men into three shifts. One third were always going to work, one third were always working, and one third were always coming from work. That way everybody got fed, though it kept the cooks pretty busy. They were always making breakfast for some, dinner for others, and supper for the rest.

Paul even invented the Northern Lights so one shift could work at night. But he gave that up because the lights weren't dependable.

Northern Lights (nôr′ THərn līts) band of colored light in the sky in the northern region

119

****

The Widow Oakley's Daughter, Annie

Frank Siedel

stagecoach
(stāj' kōch)
coach carrying
parcels and
passengers over
a regular route

The stagecoach pulled up in front of the famed Gibson Hotel in Cincinnati. The driver looked over the crowd that had gathered around. His name was Jesse Jago. Finally he spotted the manager of the hotel.

"Got a box for you here from Greenville," Jesse called out.

"Greenville? Don't know anybody in Greenville," said the manager.

"Note goes with it," Jesse said. He pulled a soiled piece of paper from his hat and handed it over.

The manager read slowly: "I am sending you five dozen quail. I hope you can use them in your hotel. A. Oakley."

quail
(kwāl)
game bird about
ten inches long

The manager read the note. Then he said, "Tell your friend at Greenville, the Gibson

****

riddled
(rid′ld)
having many
holes

birdshot
(bėrd′shot)
small lead shot
used in a
shotgun

plumb
(plum)
slang word
meaning "all the
way," or "clear"

House will never serve our guests quail. They're always riddled with birdshot." He turned away, as though to end the matter.

"All right," Jesse said, "but if I was you, I'd have a look. Might be such a thing he didn't use birdshot."

"Impossible," the manager said. He reached into the box and picked up a bird. He looked at it closely. He put it down quickly and picked up another. A moment later he turned to Jesse. "Never saw anything like it in my life. Do you know every one of these birds has been shot plumb through the head?"

"Yeah," Jesse smiled. "I know it."

"I'll take all of these birds," the manager said. "By the way, who is this hunter who can shoot sixty quail each through the head?"

"That person is A. Oakley," said Jesse.

"A friend of yours?" the manager asked.

"Yep, a good friend."

Later that year, the manager of the Gibson House waited for Jesse Jago to arrive from Greenville with the stagecoach.

"Jesse," he said, "is that A. Oakley still up in Greenville?"

"Yep," Jesse said.

"Can you get him up here?"

"What for?" Jesse asked.

The manager showed him a poster. It announced in circus-style letters the appearance of "FRANK BUTLER, WORLD'S CHAMPION RIFLE SHOT."

"Ever hear of this fellow Frank Butler?" the manager asked, pointing to the poster.

"Reckon I have," Jesse said.

"You know he has a standing offer of a hundred dollars to anybody who can outshoot him?"

"Has he now?"

"That's right. And I've bet him another hundred dollars that I know a fella who can beat him. Word's all over town. Everybody's betting on that Oakley fella. Can you get him to come up?"

"What sort of a match?"

"Rifle. Best out of a hundred."

"I'll fetch A. Oakley, providin' one thing— the match goes on no matter what Oakley's age or size or looks may be."

"I don't care what he looks like. He can shoot, that's all we care about."

"Oakley'll be here Saturday."

Never was there such a crowd on hand to greet the Greenville stage as there was that Saturday. Quail shot through the head had been the talk of Cincinnati for months. Word of it had passed up and down the river. Now it seemed that everyone was at the Gibson House for the arrival of A. Oakley.

When the stage arrived, there were only

two passengers—an athletic-looking man and a girl. The crowd closed in around the man, cheering him.

"But I'm not a sharpshooter!" he shouted. "I'm a reporter! What's going on, anyhow?"

A willowy girl stood at the side, watching. She was the girl who had just arrived on the stage. A plaid skirt hung nearly to her ankles. A sunbonnet framed her pretty face.

"I beg your pardon," she said. "I reckon I'm the one you're lookin' for. My name's Annie Oakley."

A roar of protest went up from the crowd. "A. Oakley? A woman? Oh, no!" The quick-thinkers rushed away to change their bets. The others demanded that the match be called off.

Jesse Jago came to Annie's rescue. He spoke softly, as he always did. "One of the conditions of this match was that it goes on exactly as scheduled, no matter what A. Oakley looked like. Get your gun, Annie," he said.

The rest of the story is still told on winter nights. Annie Oakley, the little girl from backwoods Ohio, fired shoulder to shoulder with the world's champion rifle shot, Frank Butler. On the last round, the one hundredth, Frank Butler missed. Annie Oakley never missed.

Had the story ended there it still would

have been told. But the Annie Oakley story was just beginning. To the delight of all future storytellers, Annie Oakley and Frank Butler fell in love. They were married a year later.

After that the posters announced, "ANNIE OAKLEY, WORLD'S CHAMPION RIFLE SHOT," and in smaller type, "Assisted by Frank Butler." It was a sensational act. It soon became the greatest single attraction in show business.

Then Annie and Frank Butler and Buffalo Bill Cody got together for a bigger and better show.

Buffalo Bill had organized a Wild West tent show. After its first few seasons, the show was deeply in debt. Buffalo Bill, like everyone else, had heard of Annie Oakley. When someone suggested that Buffalo Bill hire Annie for the show, he gave a simple, hard answer. "No! No women in my show."

Finally, the manager of the show asked Annie to come meet Buffalo Bill. He took her to the door of Buffalo Bill's tent, where she started shooting. Buffalo Bill rushed out of his tent, hopping mad. What he saw, though, stopped him in his tracks.

Frank Butler grabbed up six small balls and tossed them high into the air. Annie grabbed a rifle from the table and shot down two of them. She set that rifle down, picked up another and shot down two more. Then she changed to a third rifle. She shot the last two balls out of the air before they had touched the ground. Six balls with three different rifles! It was a masterful exhibition.

Buffalo Bill was convinced. He asked Annie Oakley to join the show. From that day, the Wild West show began breaking records. By the time it had toured the nation, Annie Oakley had become the best-loved performer around. Then the show went to Europe. The girl from backwoods Ohio gave one command performance after another before the kings and queens of Europe.

As part of her act, Annie Oakley entered the arena on a galloping white horse, shooting as she came. Buffalo Bill then tossed bundles of tickets into the air, which spread as they fell. Annie shot holes in a lot of those tickets before they reached the floor. The tickets fell among the audience. A ticket with a bullet hole through it could be turned in at the box office for a refund.

And to this day tickets for the best seats "in the house" have holes in them. And they are known the world over as "Annie Oakleys."

Round at both ends and high in the middle.

(Ohio)

command performance
(kə mand′ pər fôr′ məns)
giving of a show by request of a king, queen, or president

arena
(ə rē′ nə)
space where contests or shows take place

refund
(rē′ fund)
return of money paid

126

The Widow Oakley's Daughter, Annie

Thinking About the Story

1. Why couldn't the manager of the Gibson Hotel serve quail that was riddled with birdshot to his customers? What would birdshot do to their teeth? Why were the quail A. Oakley sent to him better?

2. Why did Jesse refer to Annie as A. Oakley? Why didn't he let on that the A. stood for Annie?

3. What kind of person do you think Annie Oakley was? How do you think she became a good shot? Did women in those days need to know how to shoot?

Doing Things

Find examples of the Wild West in today's world. Cut out pictures of western clothing that you find in magazines. Then make a list of things you see on television or in the movies. Keep a scrapbook about the Wild West.

Presidents of the Great Lakes

These ten Presidents came from the Great Lake states.

William Henry Harrison

Ulysses S. Grant

Rutherford B. Hayes

Eight From Ohio

William Henry Harrison was our ninth President. He served only 32 days in 1841. He was the first President to die in office.

Ulysses Simpson Grant was our eighteenth President. He served for eight years, from 1869 to 1877. He was a great Civil War general, and the first Ohio-born President.

Rutherford Birchard Hayes was our nineteenth President. He served from 1877 to 1881. His election was the most argued over in history. He was elected by a special electoral commission.

James Abram Garfield was our twentieth President. He served in 1881 for 199 days. He was the second President to be assassinated.

Benjamin Harrison was our twenty-third President. He served from 1889 to 1893. He was the grandson of President William Henry Harrison. He was born in Ohio, though he was elected from Indiana.

---

assassinated (ə sas′n āt əd) murdered
electoral commission (i lek′tər əl kə mish′ən) group of people who choose the President in case of problems

128

James A. Garfield

Benjamin Harrison

William McKinley

William H. Taft

Warren G. Harding

Abraham Lincoln

Gerald R. Ford

William McKinley was our twenty-fifth President. He served from 1897 to 1901. He was shot and killed by an assassin in 1901.

William Howard Taft was our twenty-seventh President. He served from 1909 to 1913. He was the first President to throw out a ball during baseball season.

Warren Gamaliel Harding was our twenty-ninth President. He served from 1921 to 1923. On June 14, 1922, he delivered the first speech ever given by a President over the radio.

One From Illinois

Abraham Lincoln was our sixteenth President. He served from 1860 to 1865. He is best known for being our "Civil War President." But he was also a wonderful storyteller. While watching a play, Lincoln was shot and killed by John Wilkes Booth. He died on April 15, 1865.

And One From Michigan

Gerald Rudolph Ford was our thirty-eighth President. He served from 1974 to 1976. He was the only man to become Vice President and later President without having been elected. He was appointed instead.

129

Festivals and Inventions

Things To Do: Pretend you are the world's greatest inventor. Draw your favorite invention and write a few sentences telling how it works. Find out about festivals and parades in your area.

Arab World Festival, Detroit, Michigan.

French voyager canoe, Old French Town Days Festival, Monroe, Michigan.

The Filipino Shoe Dance at the Holiday Folk Fair, Milwaukee, Wisconsin.

The first sousaphone, designed by John Philip Sousa, was made in Elkhart, Indiana, in 1908.

Latin American Festival, Detroit, Michigan.

Wilbur Wright was born in New Castle, Indiana and Orville Wright in Dayton, Ohio. They are shown here launching the world's first heavier-than-air craft, December 17, 1903.

An early automotive assembly line, Michigan.

An automotive assembly line today, Michigan.

An early meat-packing plant, Chicago, Illinois.

Christopher Sholes of Milwaukee, Wisconsin invented the first practical typewriter.

James Ritty of Dayton, Ohio invented the first practical cash register.

Cyrus McCormick demonstrating a mechanical reaper he made in his Chicago, Illinois factory, in 1850.

MIKE FINK, THE RIVER ROARER

Adrian Stoutenberg

The Mississippi and the Missouri rivers are usually pretty quiet these days. It was a lot different when Mike Fink was whooping up and down them in his keelboat. But then, Mike was about the noisiest thing next to thunder that this country has ever heard.

Mike was born to be a riverman, although he didn't know it until he was old enough to find out. Until then he spent his time in the woods around Pittsburgh, where he was born. He shot at wolves, bobcats, mosquitoes, or anything else that could be shot at. He wasn't especially big, but he was tough—as tough as a bale of barbed wire and as touchy as dynamite.

Mike was as good at bragging as he was at shooting and fighting. "I can shoot faster than greased lightning going through a slippery

keelboat
(kēl′bōt)
boat with one
main piece of
wood or steel
that stretches the
length of the
bottom

bale
(bāl)
large bundle
wrapped and
tied for shipping

134

thundercloud!" Mike boasted when he was still only ten years old. "I can shoot all the scales off a leaping trout with one bullet."

People who didn't know Mike too well laughed.

"I'll prove it!" Mike said. He jumped into the air, clapped his heels together, yelled "Cock-a-doodle-doo!" and loaded his long flintlock rifle at the same time. "Hold onto your hats while I find something worth shooting at," he said.

"Farmer Neal's having a big shooting contest next Sunday," a townsman told him. "If you shoot as well as you claim, you'll win a nice hunk of fresh beef. But you'll have to pay a quarter for each shot you try."

On Sunday, Mike dressed up in his best buckskin and stuck a wild turkey feather in his cap. Then he marched off to Farmer Neal's place. The silver on his rifle was polished like glass.

The field at the shooting contest was crowded with people. The men trying for the prize were soldiers and hunters, Indian scouts and boatmen. They were the best shots in the country. They grinned and winked at seeing young Mike there, and one said:

"You'd better let me lift you up so you can see the target, sonny."

"I can jump higher than a Plymouth Rock rooster and yell louder," Mike said. He gave a

scales
(skālz)
the thin, flat, outer covering of a fish

flintlock rifle
(flint′ lok rī′ fəl)
old-fashioned gun in which a spark of fire is made by flint hitting steel

buckskin
(buk′ skin)
strong, soft leather made from the skin of deer

loud crow, jumped, waved his heels, and
fired at a passing bee. The bee flipped over,
closed its eyes, and landed at Mike's feet. But
in a second, the bee sat up and buzzed.

"You didn't kill that bee, young fellow," a
man said.

"Didn't plan to," Mike said and held up the
bee. "I just snipped off his stinger so he won't
bother me when I'm aiming at the target."

When his turn came, Mike stepped up to
the firing line and got set to take his first shot.
The target was a round, white piece of paper
tacked to a board on a distant oak tree. At the
center was a circle called the bull's-eye.

No one had hit the center of the white circle
yet. Mike pulled the trigger of his rifle, called

Bang-All. It banged, and the bullet zipped straight through the bull's-eye.

People whistled in surprise, but one man said, "I'll bet you can't do that again, sonny."

Mike blew the smoke from the muzzle of Bang-All. "I paid for five shots," he said. "I'll drive every bullet right on top of the other, even with a blindfold on. For I can outshoot, outhunt, and outlick any man or mountain lion this side of the Alleghenies, and the other side too!"

"Move the target farther back!" somebody yelled.

The target was moved so far off that some of the older people had to use spyglasses to see

muzzle
(muz′əl)
the open end of
a gun

outlick
(out′lik′)
beat

Alleghenies
(al′ə gā′nēz)
Allegheny
Mountains, a
range that
stretches from
Pennsylvania to
Virginia

137

it. Mike whipped his second bullet through the heart of the target. He sent his third bullet whamming in on top of the one before. When he had hit the bull's-eye five times, the rest of the marksmen decided they might as well go home and take up knitting.

Mike went home, too, lugging five quarters of beef with him. The Fink family had enough chops and roasts for a whole winter, even though Mike could eat a dozen steaks all by himself for breakfast.

When Mike was seventeen, he started hanging around the river docks in Pittsburgh. He watched the boats. There were barges and keelboats, flatboats and Indian canoes. And there were a few ships left over from the Revolutionary War navy. Some craft carried cargoes of flour, cloth, lumber, and nails. Some carried people and livestock from one town to another. There were not many roads through the wilderness then.

Mike leaned on his six-foot-long rifle and dreamed about becoming a boatman. He watched the water churn against the sides of the river craft, sparkling like soapsuds. Best of all, he liked watching the men who ran the boats. Most of them were as powerful and as full of brag and fight as he was. A few wore red feathers in their hats. A red feather meant that the person wearing it was the roughest, toughest, hardest-to-beat riverman around.

barges
(bärj′əz)
large, flat-bottomed boats for carrying freight on rivers and canals

cargoes
(kär′gōz)
freight carried by a ship

livestock
(līv′stok)
farm animals, like cows and sheep

"I aim to get me a red feather," Mike decided. "I aim to get me all the red feathers there are, from here to the Rockies, and on the other side, too!"

Mike told his folks good-bye. Then he polished up Bang-All until it glittered like a hive of bees. He walked up to the first keelboat captain he found in Pittsburgh.

"What can you do?" the captain asked.

"There's just about nothing I can't do," said Mike, "except possibly drink up the Pacific Ocean in one swallow. Otherwise, I can out-roar a mother hurricane and all her family. I can knock down a thunderbolt with my breath and spit the Sahara Desert into a flood. In my spare time I can haul up so many whales, the Atlantic will sink a hundred feet. I can also do a few other things I can't even think of right at the moment."

"I'll try you out," said the captain, and he wrote Mike's name down on the crew list.

Mike bought himself a proper keelboatman's outfit—a red shirt, blue jacket, linsey-woolsey pants, moccasins, a fur cap, and a wide belt from which he hung a knife. He strutted on board and looked around until he saw a big-nosed man with a red feather stuck in his cap. Mike swaggered over to the man, doubled up his fists, and roared:

"Whoop, hi-ho, and a cock-a-doodle-do! I was raised in a crib with rattlesnakes, mad

the Rockies
(rok′ ēz)
the Rocky Mountains, in western North America

hive
(hīv)
house for bees to live in

linsey-woolsey pants
(lin′ zē wŭl′ zē)
strong, rough fabric made of linen and wool

scorpions
(skôr′ pē ənz)
small animals
with a poisonous
sting in their
tails

ornery
(ôr′ nėr ē)
slang word for
stubborn

scorpions, and hungry bumblebees. I'm second cousin to a hurricane, first cousin to a seven-day blizzard, and brother to an earthquake! I'm so all-fired ferocious and ornery, it scares even me to think about it! And I'm so chock-full of fight and fury, I have to lick somebody or my muscles will bust like cannon balls!"

"You may fool all the people some of the time; you can even fool some of the people all the time; but you can't fool all of the people all the time."

—Abraham Lincoln

140

The big-nosed boatman, whose name was Carpenter, puffed up his chest and roared right back at Mike, "Whoop and holler! I'm a man-eating panther! My teeth are like buzz saws and my eyes are sharp enough to bore holes through midnight. My mother was a tiger, and my father was a rhinoceros. I can crack an elephant's bones in one hand, break five grizzly bears' backs with the other, and blow down a forest with one breath. I'm so rough I don't dare scratch myself for fear my skin will come off!"

There was nothing to do but fight to prove who was the better man. The rest of the keel-boatmen watched and trembled. The boat

buzz saws
(buz sôz)
tools used to cut down trees

141

bail
(bāl)
throw water out
of a boat with a
bucket

itself trembled as Mike and Carpenter wrestled and rolled, struck and staggered, panted and puffed. They fought for two hours, sweating so hard that a few men had to bail the boat to keep everyone from drowning. Finally, Mike gave a whoop loud enough to tear a hole through the boat deck. He leaped and drove his feet into Carpenter's belly. He knocked Carpenter flat as a pancake turner.

Carpenter lay still. He said, "Whoop," but his voice was so weak that a ladybug sitting right on his chin couldn't hear it. When he gained enough strength, he stood up and gave Mike the red feather from his hat.

"Mike Fink," he said, "you're the best fighter on the Ohio, the Mississippi, the Missouri, and probably any other river in the U. S. of A."

"I don't want to brag," Mike said, "but I guess I am." He put the feather in his cap and shook Carpenter's hand.

The two felt so friendly that they promised they would die for each other, if they absolutely had to. In between fighting and friendship-making, which amounted to the same thing,

Mike learned how to be a regular keelboat-man. He learned how to ram a long pole down to the bottom of the river and push the boat upstream against the current. He learned to watch out for sandbars or snags that could stop the boat. He could see a dead tree floating in the water almost before it died and dropped there.

By the time Mike had been on the river a while, he had so many red feathers in his cap that he threw most of them away. He was afraid people would think he was a bonfire!

There were lazy times on the river, too, when Mike and his friend Carpenter would stretch out on the deck and watch the sun go by. Sometimes they would fish for catfish or sit on shore at night studying a campfire.

On one of those lazy days, Mike felt the need for a little extra target practice. He took a tin cup full of cider, handed it to Carpenter, and said, "Pace off about sixty yards and set that cup on your head. I'll shoot it off."

Carpenter looked a bit nervous, but he did as he was told. Mike aimed Bang-All and fired. The bullet whistled through the cup's brim, not spilling a drop. Carpenter took his turn with the same trick. He hit the cup on Mike's head, but he spilled some of the cider.

From then on, Mike and Carpenter would show off their trick to all the other boatmen.

sandbars
(sand′bärz)
ridges of sand formed by the currents in the river

snags
(snagz)
trees or branches held fast in a river

bonfire
(bon′fīr)
fire built outdoors

143

One time, before Mike could fire at the cup on Carpenter's head, there was a blast from another rifle in the woods nearby. The cup flew into the air.

Mike spun around so fast the ground smoked. "Who did that?" he roared.

"My name's Talbot," a man said, stepping out of the woods. He was a red-headed fellow with muscles bunched up as thick as thunderclouds.

"Whoop, holler, and hailstones!" Mike yelled, jumping into the air and banging his heels together. "I'm the original meat-grinder, muscle-ripper, and the meanest, cruelest creation that ever drew breath!"

Talbot took a deep breath and shouted back, "Whoop! I'm the man who invented fighting. I've got fists so big they make mountains look like bumps. I've got a hide like an alligator and a heart as black as a buzzard in a coal mine!"

They leaped at each other. They hissed and hollered. They slammed and rolled and punched. The ground shook, and the trees shook until all the leaves fell off. At last, after several hours, Mike swung his fist up from the ground. His knuckles banged Talbot's chin so hard that Talbot flew up and hit his head on a tree branch. When he sailed down to earth again, his head was considerably flatter, and all the fight had gone out of him.

buzzard
(buz′ərd)
kind of vulture

Talbot and Mike shook hands. When the men went back onto the keelboat, Talbot went along. He, Carpenter, and Mike all swore they would die for each other, if they absolutely had to.

With three mighty men like that fighting for each other and whooping up and down the rivers, it seemed there was no one they couldn't lick. But there was. The man who had them licked wasn't even very good with his fists, and he didn't whoop and holler at all. His name was Robert Fulton, and all he did to become the new ruler of the river was invent the steamboat.

Mike hated steamboats even more than he hated to sit still. Every time he saw one coming, its big side-wheels churning the water, he shook his fists at the sky. But the steamboats kept on coming, getting bigger and faster. They pushed the keelboats out of the way and won every race.

Mike still worked on the keelboats, but it wasn't like the old days. He wasn't the real boss of the river any more. And Pittsburgh, St. Louis, and New Orleans were growing too civilized for his liking.

That's how Mike happened to leave the rivers and become a mountain man. But that's another whoop, holler, and cock-a-doodle-doo! I'll have to tell you about that some other time.

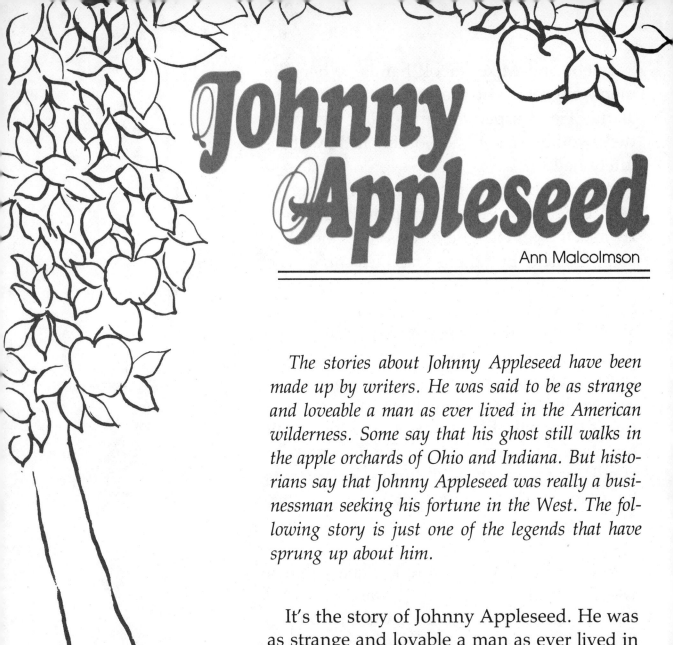

Johnny Appleseed

Ann Malcolmson

The stories about Johnny Appleseed have been made up by writers. He was said to be as strange and loveable a man as ever lived in the American wilderness. Some say that his ghost still walks in the apple orchards of Ohio and Indiana. But historians say that Johnny Appleseed was really a businessman seeking his fortune in the West. The following story is just one of the legends that have sprung up about him.

It's the story of Johnny Appleseed. He was as strange and lovable a man as ever lived in the American wilderness.

Appleseed, of course, wasn't his real name. His parents proudly named him Jonathan— Jonathan Chapman. Young Johnny Chapman spent his boyhood playing in the woods and on the farms near his home in Boston.

146

As he grew strong and healthy, two things became clear to him. First, he was a born orchardman. He understood trees, especially fruit trees. Second, he was going West. He had heard tales of the wonderful rich country behind the Pennsylvania mountains. It was the country of Daniel Boone and the other pioneers. Johnny planned on seeing it. So as a young man he went to Pittsburgh and bought himself a little farm. There he planted an orchard.

At that time Pittsburgh was West. Nevertheless it wasn't far enough West for Johnny. Day by day, people passed his farm. They came on foot and on horseback. They came in rickety farm wagons and in handsome coaches. They were all bound for the wilderness of the Ohio Valley. Some of them stopped at his door to ask for water, or food or a night's lodging. To all of them Johnny gave what he could.

Johnny felt sorry for these people. He knew how lonely they were going to be to be without the towns and pleasant farmlands they had left behind. He wanted to help them. But how could he, a poor nurseryman, do it? Sometimes he had hardly enough to eat himself.

One night his question answered itself. He'd give them all apple orchards. So he did.

orchard
(ôr′chərd)
piece of ground on which fruit trees are grown

rickety
(rik′ə tē)
shaky

coaches
(kōch′ iz)
large, old-fashioned, closed carriages with seats inside

nurseryman
(nėr′sər ē mən)
person who grows young trees and plants

mash
(mash)
squashed fruit
pulp

cider presses
(sī' dər pres' əz)
machines used to
squeeze the juice
from apples

To every traveler who stopped at his cabin, he gave a bag of apple seeds. The pioneers were nearly always grateful. They wrote home to their friends about the generous man near Pittsburgh.

Soon Johnny had given away all the seeds he could spare. He started bothering his neighbors. Most of them were gruff Pennsylvania Dutchmen. They thought their young friend was a little crazy. But they were glad enough to give him the mash that was left in their cider presses, if he could use that. He worked hard, picking out the seeds from the sticky mess. He collected the seeds and put them in bags and pouches—enough seeds to plant an orchard.

For the next forty years until he died, Johnny had no home of his own. He paddled his little canoe up the creeks and backwaters. Whenever he found a likely spot he stopped. He cleared away the underbrush and planted some apple seeds. Then he built a fence around his plot, to keep the deer from nibbling the first tender shoots—and off he went again. Several times he ran out of the seeds. He had to go back to Pennsylvania for more cider mash, to be dried and sorted and packed in pouches for more orchards.

Now and then when new settlers moved into the countryside, Johnny "sold" them the

148

saplings from his forest plots. If they had money he charged "a fib-penny bit" for each tree. But usually he took old clothes as a swap, or let the pioneers "buy" the orchards with promises to pay him later.

He didn't make much money, but that didn't worry him. He didn't need much money. He liked sleeping out in the open. He never wore shoes, even in the worst blizzards. At first he wore the cast-off clothes he received for his young trees. After a while, even these became too civilized. So he begged an old coffee sack from a storekeeper. He cut a hole for his head and two for his arms, and let it go at that. Hats were a nuisance, too. Since he had to carry a kettle to cook his cornmeal in, he solved the problem by wearing the kettle on his head.

He had no gun and no hunting knife. Not even the Indians, those master woodsmen, could understand this fact. Johnny, however, lived well on berries and apples and roots and the cornmeal mush he stirred up in his "hat."

What about shelter? Many an old settler will tell you that when Johnny was invited to spend the winter night in front of his cabin fire, Johnny shook his head politely. He said he'd rather sleep out in the open with his friends, the animals.

saplings
(sap′lingz)
young trees

fib-penny bit
(fib′pen ē bit′)
Spanish coin worth about 6¢; used in eastern U.S. until 1857

cast-off
(kast′ôf)
thrown away

lean-tos
(lēn′ tüz)
rough sheds or
shelters

medicine man
(med′ ə sən
man′)
man believed by
the North
American
Indians to have
magic power
over disease

brave
(brāv)
North American
Indian warrior

This strange little man was a welcome guest in all the tepees, lean-tos, and cabins in the Ohio Territory. Wherever he went, he managed to carry little presents for the settlers. There were usually seeds and herbs for the grown-ups. He brought bits of calico for the little girls, and odd pebbles and shells for the boys.

But best of all he had a stock of stories. In the wilderness, news was scarce. The pioneers rarely had news of the neighbors who lived five miles away. They rarely had news from back home or news of what was happening in the world. Johnny talked and listened to everyone he met. In time he became a sort of living newspaper and postman for the people in the wilderness.

The boys, of course, liked most to hear him tell about his life with the Indians. The Shawnees still lived in the Ohio country. Not many of the white settlers had much to do with them. But Johnny actually lived with them. The Shawnees thought he was a medicine man.

Once, while camping in the forest, Johnny met an Indian who was suffering from a fever. Johnny knew what plants could be used to cure illnesses. In a day or so he had cured the brave. From that time on, the Indian was his friend. He even asked Johnny to visit his camp.

Johnny was as good an Indian as any of them. So he was made a member of the Shawnee tribe. Throughout the whole West he was known as the Indian's friend.

Many of the stories he told the settlers were about his adventures with animals. He dearly loved all living things. The animals seemed to understand this, and some people thought he understood animal-talk.

One chilly night he was walking through the woods when he began to feel sleepy. He picked out a hollow log and started to crawl in. Unfortunately, a honey bear had had the same idea. All at once, Johnny touched something soft and furry. He heard an angry growl only a foot from his head. You and I might have been frightened. But not Johnny Appleseed. He apologized politely to the bear and backed out of the log. Then he found himself another shelter in the crook of a tree.

For several years Johnny had a pet wolf who followed him wherever he went. This was a strange pet indeed, especially in the frontier country. Wolves were hated and feared. But this wolf was different. Johnny had found it caught in a trap. Its heavy iron jaw had cut the wolf's leg. Johnny walked

crook
(krŭk)
curved or bent part of something

frontier
(frun tir')
last edge of settled country, where the wilds begin

151

fearlessly up to the snarling beast and soothed it. Unafraid, he opened the jaws of the trap and set the animal free. Then he bound up the wounded leg. He brought water from a nearby spring and gave the wolf a drink from his old mush-kettle hat. He treated the wolf as though it were a sick baby.

As the sore healed, the wolf began to follow Johnny. It padded behind him in the woods and watched over him at night. The wolf was the orchardman's friend and favorite. But one day an angry farmer, mistaking the wolf for the thief in his chicken yard, shot it.

As the years went by Johnny's saplings grew into large trees. New settlers moved in and cleared the land. The wilderness became a rich farming country, crossed with roads and dotted with villages. Things became too civilized for the strange little man.

So he moved West with the frontier into Indiana and Michigan and Illinois. In his coffee-sack shirt and his mush-kettle hat, he continued planting his seeds in the forest and carrying his news.

One day many years later a farmer found his worn-out old body lying beside a little orchard in the woods near Fort Wayne, Indiana. Johnny had died looking after his beloved trees.

Mike Fink, the River Roarer/
Johnny Appleseed

Thinking About the Stories

1. How were Johnny Appleseed and Mike Fink alike? How were they different?
2. Johnny Appleseed was a special person. Find passages in the story to support this statement. Would Johnny have been able to carry on his work if he lived in America today?
3. Why do you think Mike Fink needed to fight with people? Do you think it made them better friends?
4. Mike Fink was "one of the biggest braggarts that ever lived." Look back in the story to find Mike's brags.

Doing Things

1. Carry on the legend of Johnny Appleseed. Plant fruit seeds in flower pots. See if they will grow.
2. Can you brag? Think about funny brags you can make about yourself. Have a bragging contest with a friend or classmate.
3. Ask in your library for stories about other legendary heroes, such as Davy Crockett. Share your favorite legend with the class.

Indian Voices of the Great Lakes

It is I who wear the morning star
on my forehead. . . .
All that grows upon the earth
is mine.

                              Iroquois

I
of the owl
am afraid
whenever I am sitting alone
in the wigwam.

                              Ojibwa

A loon I thought it was,
But it was
my love's splashing oar.

                              Ojibwa

Tecumseh, the chief from a Shawnee tribe, was a great leader of his people. In 1810, General Harrison told him the government wanted to buy more Indian land. Tecumseh answered, "Sell a country! Why not sell the air, the great sea, as well as the earth?"

Great Lakes State Fare

ILLINOIS: "The Land of Lincoln;" "The Inland Empire"

State Motto: "State Sovereignty, National Union"

Main Industries:

Manufacturing: machinery, electrical equipment, food and food products, primary and fabricated metals, chemical products, precision instruments

Mining: coal, petroleum, stone

Agriculture: corn, soybeans, dairy products, wheat, oats, hay, cattle, hogs

State Flower:
Native Violet

State Bird:
Cardinal

State Tree:
White Oak

INDIANA: "The Hoosier State"

State Motto: "The Crossroads of America"

State Flower:
Peony

State Tree:
Tulip Tree

State Bird:
Cardinal

Main Industries:

Manufacturing: electrical equipment, steel manufacturing, transportation equipment, food and food products
Mining: coal, petroleum, sand and gravel, stone
Agriculture: corn, wheat, sorghum, beef cattle, dairy products, hogs, sheep, poultry

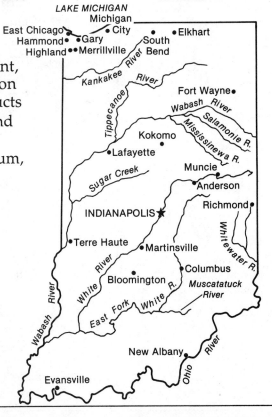

OHIO: "The Buckeye State"

Main Industries:

Manufacturing: transportation equipment, machinery, primary and fabricated metal products, food processing, chemicals
Mining: coal, petroleum, limestone, natural gas, sand and gravel, clay
Agriculture: corn, hay, wheat, oats, soybeans, beef cattle, hogs, sheep, poultry

State Motto:
"With God all things are possible."

State Flower:
Scarlet Carnation

State Tree:
Ohio Buckeye

State Bird:
Cardinal

MICHIGAN: "The Wolverine State"

State Motto: *"Si quaeris peninsulam amoenam, circumspice."*
(If you seek a pleasant peninsula, look about you.)

Main Industries:

Manufacturing: transportation equipment, cars, machine tools, chemicals, food and food products, metals, plastics

Mining: crude petroleum, iron ore, cement, natural gas, sand and gravel

Agriculture: corn, wheat, soybeans, dairy products, beef cattle

State Flower:
Apple Blossom

State Tree:
White Pine

State Bird:
Robin

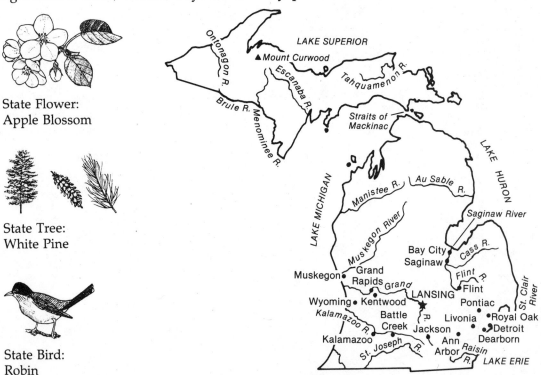

WISCONSIN: "The Badger State"

State Motto: "Forward"

Main Industries:
Manufacturing: machinery, food and related products, fabricated metals, transportation equipment, paper and related products
Mining: sand and gravel, iron, cement, crushed stone, lime
Agriculture: dairy products, corn, beans, beets, beef cattle, hogs, honey, mink

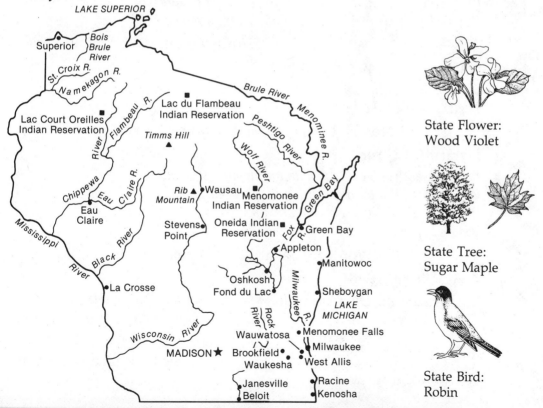

State Flower: Wood Violet

State Tree: Sugar Maple

State Bird: Robin

Great Lakes Sing-Along

Illinois

By thy rivers gently flowing, Illinois, Illinois,
O'er thy prairies verdant growing, Illinois, Illinois,
Comes an echo on the breeze,
Rustling through the leafy trees.

Words by Charles H. Chamberlain Music by Archibald Johnson

Indiana

On the Banks of the Wabash, Far Away
Round my Indiana homestead wave the cornfields,
In the distance loom the woodlands near and cool.
Oftentimes my thoughts revert to scenes of childhood,
Where I first received my lessons, nature's school.

Words and music by Paul Dresser

Michigan, My Michigan

The whisper of the forest tree,   *Unite in one grand symphony*
The thunder of the inland sea,   *Of Michigan, my Michigan.*

Words by Douglas Malloch Music by W. Otto Miessner

Beautiful Ohio

Drifting with the current down a moonlit stream,
While above the Heavens in their glory gleam.
Beautiful Ohio, in dreams again I see,
Visions of what used to be.

Words by Ballard MacDonald Music by Mary Earl

On, Wisconsin!

On, Wisconsin! On, Wisconsin!   *We, thy loyal sons and daughters,*
Grand old badger state!   *Hail thee good and great.*

Words by J. S. Hubbard and Charles D. Rosen
Music by William T. Purdy

Excerpts of official state songs